Belfast, City of Song

Belfast from River Lagan

BELFAST
CITY of SONG

edited by
MAURICE LEYDEN
with a foreword by
DAVID HAMMOND

BRANDON

To Jane and my mother

First published in 1989 by
Brandon Book Publishers Ltd.
Dingle, Co. Kerry, Ireland

British Library Cataloguing in Publication Data
Belfast, city of song.
 1. Folk songs in Irish: Northern Irish Folk songs
 I. Leyden, Maurice
 784.4'9416

 ISBN 0 86322 110 6

The publisher acknowledges the financial assistance of the Arts
Council of Northern Ireland in the publication of this volume.

Cover design by The Graphiconies, Dublin
Cover illustration by Leonard Sheil
Internal design by Brandon, Dingle
Typesetting by Seton Music Graphics, Bantry
Printed by Richard Clay Ltd, Bungay

A word a line
You may say are mine
But the best in the songs
Whatever it be
To you and to me
And to no one belongs.

William Allingham

DONEGALL PLACE, BELFAST.

Donegall Place

Contents

Acknowledgements

I am extremely grateful to the following people who helped me enormously in the preparation of this book.

Tony Knox who gave me great encouragement in the early days of the project with the radio programme *The Cavehill Diamond;* John Moulden who offered advice, encouragement and valuable references throughout the project, and Jackie Dixon and Neil Johnston for their enthusiasm and interest. David Hammond and John Gray read the script and gave me useful advice on the general presentation.

Thanks to my wife Jane for typing, for painstakingly stencilling the music and for moral support, and to my mother, who also helped with the typing. Thanks also to Paddy Finney, Janet Harbison, and Neil Martin for scoring the music; to Trevor Stewart for *His Lordship Had A Coachman* and *The Cotton Mill Song;* to Chris Jobling for the words of *The Kinnegar;* to Hugh Shields for the words of *Young McCance,* and to Helen Creighton for the music of *The Sailor's Hornpipe In Caxon Street.*

I am grateful to Mrs Craig, daughter of Sam Henry, for permission to publish the words and music of *The Belfast Mountains, Belfast Town* and *Campbell's Mill,* and the music of *The Lady Of The Lake* and *Divis Mountain. Henry Joy McCracken* is published by kind permission of Pan Books Ltd.

I am deeply indebted to the following libraries and their staffs for making their material so readily available and for permission to publish the songs: Cambridge University Library for *The Belfast Lass, Lovely Ann* and *The Lady of the Lake;* Belfast Central Library for *The Brave Queen's Island Boys;* Queen's University, Belfast, for the words of *The Sailor's Hornpipe In Caxon Street* and *The Shipwreck On The Lagan Canal;* the Vaughan Williams Memorial Library, London, for *The Orange Riots In Belfast* from a photocopy in their possession, and the British Library, London, for *The Belfast Mountains (1810), The New Tramway, The Tramway Line, The Young Man Badly Walked, The Connaught Man's Trip To Belfast, The Sights And Scenes Of Belfast* and *A New Song.*

My sincerest thanks to the Linenhall Library, Belfast, and its staff for their excellent service and interest in the project, and for permission to publish *The Cavehill Diamond* (both versions), *Gas Lights, His Lordship Had A Coachman, The Charming Belfast Lass, The Maid Of Belfast Town, The Belfast Cockabendy, Roving Jack The Baker, The Ports Are Open, Annie Moore* and *The Battle Of The Navvies.* Thanks also to the National Library of Ireland and the Royal Irish Academy, and to the Ulster Museum, Belfast, for kindly granting permission to reproduce the photographs and prints.

My thanks to the Arts Council of Northern Ireland for financial assistance in the research and publication; to Ciaran Carson and particularly Michael Longley for taking a personal interest in the project.

FOREWORD

Belfast from Knockbreda

These songs spring from the streets and the lanes of Belfast; they are redolent of the mill stack, the shipyard gantry, the square sett and the redbrick terrace. There's nothing from the more usual haunts of folk-songs, nothing from the woodland glade or the silvery lake. The songs in this collection are smoky in their textures, with a salty, northern consistency, their language clipped and consonental, their themes urban.

They are songs of the nineteenth century and Maurice Leyden has spent several years digging them up from old ballad sheets, chap-books, newspapers and the like, to present them here in their historical and social contexts. He has remained wide in his acceptance of many genres of songs, generous in his definition of the term "folk-song" so that, for instance, neither the music hall nor the literary compositions have been excluded.

Hardly any are in currency now. When they were in currency in the last century they were the songs of the people, hardly known, except maybe for the literary compositions, to the professional and mercantile classes, the establishment. For they were part of a subterranean culture and couched in the language of the street and the kitchen; expressions of the time, as the poet John Hewitt said, "before the schoolroom tamed their lively tongue".

I remember twenty odd years ago when that notable Belfast singing family, the McPeakes, won a Gold Medal at a Berlin festival for their performance of Belfast music and song. The master of ceremonies remarked, "Your Burgomaster in Belfast will be much pleased with your prize".

Francie McPeake truthfully replied, "Our Burgomaster in Belfast doesn't even know we're here".

The burghers, merchants and other entrepreneurs of nineteenth century Belfast put their belief in progress, and Belfast then was an outstanding example of Victorian zeal in its phenomenal growth. There was huge energy at work in the creation of the new industrial town, spawning a shipyard, a ropeworks and a linen industry that were all to become in a few short years the biggest in the world. They even had a conviction that God was anointing the work and that He would make the workers more punctual, more diligent, more committed to their version of wealth. They transformed Belfast from a small market town magnificently set in a ring of hills at the head of a quiet sea-lough into an eyesore. Alongside prosperity and wealth there were bad housing, disease and low wages, and the pace of change was frantic as thousands fled the countryside and tramped the city streets in search of jobs. Strangely, there is no mention of this distress in the songs: if the songmakers were aware of the squalor and the exploitation they never breathed a word.

However, this collection does reflect the jostle of change in songs like *The New Tramway,* a jaunty celebration of technical innovation. And in case we might be in danger of describing that celebration of novelty as quaint or naïve, we ought to remind ourselves how similar we are when it comes to novelty today. Build a shopping centre on the fringe of Belfast and the population of four counties will be swarming around it like clegs on the opening day. And Paul Muldoon describes in his poem "The Sightseers" how his family bundled into a rickety car in the 1960s for a day's outing to the latest sign of progress, the new roundabout at Ballygawley.

Nevertheless we have our own difficulties with the pace of change. We seem to have a genuine need to be reminded that there is a past, when people's lives used to be simpler, less hurried, less complicated. We search for a freedom from commercial, economic and political pressures. Our forebears in the Belfast of the nineteenth century, still rooted in their quieter, rural ways, were not all that different. In the bustling city streets they pined for innocence and first love, for the glamour of the lost fields, in songs like *Young McCance* and *The Maid Of Belfast Town.* These songs are expressions that are infinitely more enduring and more human than our flimsy attempts to engage our own lost past through fashionable stripped pine and oil lamps.

So, here is Maurice Leyden's collection of Belfast songs, some of first love and innocence, some of dearly-bought experience, a few family heirlooms and treasured possessions, songs of the hearth and the home as well as the music hall and stage. We welcome them with pleasure and gratitude, saluting Maurice's fondness for the songs and his dedication to his quest. The texts and the tunes breathe the personality of this odd, distressed city and the spirit of the people who have lived for years on the banks of the Lagan.

The lips may fade and die,
But the song lives on forever.

DAVID HAMMOND

INTRODUCTION

Braunan del Dec 1841
Commercial Buildings at Belfast.

The Five Corners

A story is told about a man on a bus who was spitting so much that the conductor asked him to refrain from such a disgusting habit. The man glared at the conductor and replied vehemently:

"I come from Tandragee an' I'll spit where I like."

Coming from Tandragee gives him the right to do what he wants, where he wants, when he wants. And it is this deep-rooted sense of identity and unshakeable pride of place that permeates traditional song.

"Drumquin you're not a city but you're all the world to me."

"Ardboe your equal ne'er could I find."

It is generally understood that there is nowhere "in this wide world" that can compare with home, and no matter how hard or how far you may look "the world o'er" for a better place the conclusion is always the same: "your equal ne'er could I find". There is hardly a town or townland that does not have its eulogy, and the relationship between the singer and his birthplace is a very personal one.

Before the industrial revolution transformed Belfast and its hinterland, ballad singers sold their ballad sheets on the streets and in the country-side. The printed song partially fulfilled the function of a newspaper, as there was no locally produced newspaper until the founding, in 1737, of *The Belfast News Letter and General Advertiser.* In 1718 – when the town's population stood at just two thousand five hundred – a meeting of the General Synod of the Church of Ireland complained that "there are several obscene ballads printed in Belfast and dispers'd through the country". They resolved to approach the printers "to advise them not to print such papers in the future".

In 1785 the *Belfast Mercury* published the following letter:

A lover of Decency hopes that the worthy Chief Magistrate of Belfast will exert his authority to prevent impious ballad singers from screeching immoral obscene songs and gathering crowds of unthinking people in the most public streets every evening from seven till nine o'clock.

In 1816 the *News Letter* commented that

the town has been sadly amazed by itinerant ballad singers who collect crowds of people especially at each end of Bridge Street, so that passengers cannot get forward.

In spite of protests the ballad singer was, until the early part of this century, a constant voice in an ever-changing environment. He was viewed by the authorities with suspicion, as a person likely to cause a breach of the peace and a constant threat to good moral standards.[1] He was often arrested for singing and selling seditious ballads.[2] A figure of defiance, the ballad singer turned up anywhere a crowd of people had gathered. He demanded attention by singing topical and often controversial songs. He delivered his songs by brute force in noisy streets, fairs and marketplaces in the hope that people would buy his ballad sheets. His songs brought news from the wars of victories and defeats. He sang of love and death, of emigration, politics and local events. The songs depended on mass appeal to keep them alive and if they proved popular they survived to be sung for years. Many fell by the wayside of popular acclaim but nevertheless lie preserved for posterity on the printed page. All human emotions are indelibly captured on these flimsy, crudely printed ballad sheets, in words that are a social history and melodies that embody the voices of people from another century.

Ballad sheets were not the sole source of printed songs. Throughout the 1700s chapbooks were published; these were small pamphlets measuring approximately five-and-a-half by three-and-a-half inches, unlike ballad sheets which were single sheets of about ten by eight inches. Chapbooks were more substantial in their contents, which included historical narratives, romantic and moral tales and religious sermons. Special anthology chapbooks, or "garlands", were devoted solely to songs. These contained about eight pages with between two and four songs; like the ballad sheets they were cheap and badly printed on poor quality paper with a simple woodcut illustration on the front cover of each.

The chapbooks were at the height of their popularity during the first thirty years of the nineteenth century, but by 1850 they had all but expired. Many garlands were printed locally by firms such as James Magee of Bridge Street (1730-90) and James Smyth of High Street (1800-50), and there were other publishers of chapbooks throughout the province, in Monaghan, Newry, Downpatrick and Strabane. The chapbooks were distributed by chapmen, hawkers and pedlars who, like the ballad singers, travelled through the countryside selling their wares. They were regarded with suspicion and were generally looked on as being of low degree, but they differed from the ballad singers in that they did not sing, nor did their garlands contain any inflammatory or seditious material. Consequently they were not as colourful or controversial as the ballad singers and did not incur the wrath of the authorities and the local press. What brought about their demise was the abolition in 1861 of restrictive duties on newspapers which sounded the death knell of the ballad sheets and chapbooks as cheaper newspapers became more widely available.

Chapbooks and ballad sheets were published without music. In the case of well-known songs the tunes would have been familiar to many people; in other cases the name of a popular tune might be given as a suggestion,[3] and sometimes a local singer would compose a melody to accompany a ballad, or adapt a familiar tune; thus many songs became associated with one melody.

Apart from the street ballads, entertainment in nineteenth-century Belfast was largely confined to drama in the theatres and singing in the saloons. Samuel Elliott described a visit to a Smithfield singing saloon in the 1850s:

> To gain admission to the singing saloons, you simply required to enter, sit down, and call for a penny glass of beer (potale would best name the beverage) when you could witness the performance of banjo and bones;[4] but in doing so, you were required to lose no time in disseminating the contents of your glass, as the etiquette of the waiters, who were continually lifting it up from before you, demanded the speedy ejection of the liquor as a necessary introduction to another pennyworth, which it was imperative you should repeatedly order, as otherwise funds could not be obtained by the proprietor to satisfy the claims, by way of salary, of the classic artists engaged for your amusement at an enormous expense.[5]

With the rapid growth of the town and the influx of so many people into Belfast there was a demand for new forms of entertainment in addition to those offered by the theatres and singing saloons. In 1840 a new urban phenomenon, already a huge success in London, finally arrived in Belfast: the first music hall opened, in May Street.

Music hall was regarded by many as a cheap, vulgar burlesque form of entertainment for the working classes, but there was no denying its mass appeal. It had its own inimitable style; the topical, humorous and "over the top" content of many of the songs and the catchy sing-along melodies proved irresistible to audiences. For the first time singing could be enjoyed *en masse*. Popular artists from England could now come on tour and some attracted huge crowds as well as large fees for their efforts. It was a strange hybrid of entertainment drawing on several varied sources.

Broadside singers from the streets and drawing-room ballad singers joined company with the musicians from the pleasure gardens and glee clubs, and "rooms" where these once separate elements could all be catered for began to appear.[6]

Many of the artists drew on the folk-song tradition for their repertoires. Some achieved fame and fortune in a very short time. Amongst the favourites of the new audiences were Sam Collins (1826-65), best known for his renditions of *The Rocky Road To Dublin, Paddy's Wedding* and *The Limerick Races;* Sam Cowell (1819-64) who sang *Villikins And Dinah* and *The Rat-Catcher's Daughter;* all songs that are still well known. One of the biggest stars was W.G. Ross, a Glaswegian, who won outstanding notoriety in the 1840s with one song which outraged many in his audiences with its blasphemous refrain, "damn your eyes". He sang *Sam Hall* with such "brutal ferocity and pent-up fury" that for years afterwards its performance alone would ensure packed halls wherever he went.

In the world of the music halls fortunes could be quickly made but they could also be even more quickly lost, and the comical public faces of the performers could not mask the appalling tragedy which afflicted so many of them. The pressures of public life took their toll and many performers died young. Sam Collins died at thirty-nine, Sam Cowell at forty-five, George Leybourne at forty-four, Jenny Hill at forty-six and Bessie Bellwood at thirty-nine.

As the nineteenth century progressed music hall drew on other, disparate musical sources. Black American music gave rise to black-faced minstrels singing imitation "negro" songs, and so-called "nigger minstrel entertainment" became hugely successful from the 1830s right up to modern times. Drawing-room ballads and even opera went into the melting pot of music hall. Some songs enjoyed such widespread popularity that eventually they began to find their way into traditional song repertoires. The wheel had come full circle from the early days when music hall had drawn extensively on the folk tradition. Two fine songs that are perfect examples of the music hall genre are *His Lordship Had A Coachman* and *The New Tramway.* Even today the singing tradition is peppered with music hall songs and most traditional singers will have at least one if not several songs which are a legacy from the age of the music hall.

But what of the mainstream oral singing tradition, the natural passing on of songs from generation to generation?

It was not until the early nineteenth century that folk-music was annotated. Collectors like Bunting (1773-1843), Petrie (1789-1866) and Piggott (1822-71) collected over four thousand Irish melodies but they generally ignored song texts and it was not until the end of the century that P.W. Joyce and Alfred Graves published songs complete with melody and full text. In the twentieth century Sam Henry collected about eight hundred songs which he published in the "Songs of the People" column in the *Northern Constitution* between 1925 and 1938. In the 1930s Colm Ó Lochlainn published over two hundred songs with melody and text, mostly nineteenth-century ballads. On the basis of the amounts of material amassed by the collectors, the oral tradition was, even at the end of the nineteenth century, in a very healthy state.

Another pointer to the strength of the song tradition is the repertoire of our own time: of people like Robert Cinnamond, Bridget Tunney, Joe Holmes, Eddie Butcher and Sarah Makem, all of them "big Ulster singers" born around the turn of the century whose large repertoires are a legacy from previous generations. They are not isolated examples from their communities but the very epitome of a thriving oral tradition which stretches back through the centuries.

At the beginning of the nineteenth century the people who flooded into Belfast from the surrounding counties in search of work brought their songs and folklore with them. In their new homes many lived for the first time in streets, with next-door neighbours only a wall's thickness away. Music and song was their touchstone in the unfamiliar surroundings of the town. Urban life was new to them, with its shops, streets, alleys, mills, factories, inns, taverns, theatres and public transport – experiences and sights far removed from the tranquil character of rural life. As these surroundings became more familiar and Belfast became home, town life began to percolate into folk-song. The images of mountains, rivers and lakes were replaced by the features of an urban landscape:

"As walking up by Carrick Hill..."

"Whilst walking down thru Castle Street..."

"As walking down by York Street Mill..."

"He works with me in Campbell's Mill..."

"As I was walking up North Street..."

Public transport was celebrated in the songs:

"There's a vehicle on wheels they call a Belfast Tram..."

"I hope you all may give a call on the New Tramway..."

Love songs abounded:

"It was beautiful Mary of sweet Belfast Town..."

And the seedier side of town life was also described:

"Begone you dirty drunken sot where e'er you drank your brandy..."

"A thousand lies to her I told all for to get her money..."

The love songs that people had brought with them from their country birthplaces were easily adapted to the new urban landscape simply by changing placenames. Alternatively new love songs were composed using the predictable pattern of the genre and decorated with placenames local to Belfast. The songs now placed the singers in a new setting and demonstrated a new pride of place with their celebrations of "my habitation in sweet Belfast Town" and "Belfast Town of high renown".

The urban folk-song tradition had been born and many songs in praise of Belfast appeared:

"I'm young McCance, I come from the Falls..."

"And Mill Street is a bonny place..."

"She is the darlin' of my heart and the pride of the Springfield Road..."

A new Belfast song tradition grew with the development of the town to such an extent that the life-span of a song became intrinsically linked with the pulse of the town. In essence an urban folk cycle had evolved whereby songs came into being with new industries, were popular while the industries thrived, and disappeared when those industries went into decline. That is one of the reasons why so few Belfast songs survived: nobody wanted to sing mill songs when there was chronic unemployment, and nobody wanted to sing about horse trams when there were gleaming new electric trams that were faster and smoother. Another reason why Belfast songs disappeared was because they did not travel beyond the boundaries of the town, due to the parochial nature and content of the songs. Like the ballad sheets, a lot of songs were ephemeral, written to suit an occasion and forgotten when the occasion had passed.

Love songs were an exception: some did survive to be published further afield. It was universality of theme that made them more accessible to wider audiences. *The Belfast Mountains* was published in London and in Newcastle-upon-Tyne, and *My Charming Belfast Lass* was published in Manchester.

The songs which survive in printed form provide an invaluable contribution to social history and a direct link with previous generations of ordinary people without the interference of the historian. In David Hammond's words, folk-songs embody "the history of the people told by the people".

Few Belfast songs are sung nowadays, but that is the nature of a folk tradition in an urban environment. An industrial city like Belfast changes at such a rate that industries and songs quickly become obsolete, but the songs vividly depict the life and times of the people of nineteenth-century Belfast and embody their hopes, aspirations and dreams.

CAVEHILL

A diamond bright, that shone by night, did often glitter there.

The Cavehill Diamond

Cavehill

Had I but all the diamonds,
That on the rocks do grow,
I'd give them to my Irish laddie
If he to me his love would show.

This is a verse from a song, *The Belfast Mountains,* printed in about 1810 by J. Catnach in London, and at first sight it appears to have no more significance than the thousands of other verses published by Catnach at that time. However, within these four lines is a clue to a mystery that continually aroused interest and fascination throughout the nineteenth century and early twentieth century. The mystery centred around the existence of a diamond embedded in the face of Cavehill which became known as "the Cavehill Diamond". Whether or not the diamond ever existed is still a contentious point and perhaps cynics were right to dismiss it as a chunk of limestone. The balladeers, however, were in no doubt that it existed and they were quick to embody the theme of the diamond in songs of the time, as in the above verse.

In the "Random Notes and Notions" column of *Ulster's Saturday Night* on 23 February 1895, the following reference appeared:

There used to be some curious stories told about the Cave Hill diamond before it was unearthed. One was that mariners entering Belfast Lough used to be dazzled by its glints and used to set their course by its brilliance. Then there was a legend that Finn McCool... used to wear it on his watch guard until he dropped it one day and in disgust deserted Cave Hill forever. I know the man who found the Cave Hill diamond.

Thirty years later, on 12 June 1925, the same column printed a full and detailed account of the diamond and of the geologist who had dug it up at midnight:

It was indeed a monstrous gem to be weighed in pounds avoirdupois and not by the orthodox carat. It formed the chief decoration of a draper's not a jeweller's window, where at night by its beams, it made even the unbleached calico look like something which might grace the limbs of royalty itself.

On 16 March 1926 J.S. Crone wrote in the *Belfast Telegraph:*

There was a tradition current in my youth, that there was a diamond in the Cave Hill... It was said to have shone in the face of the cliff and that vessels in the lough had fired on it to secure the precious jewel.

But the final words of an article published in *Ireland's Saturday Night* on 17 June 1920 remain as apposite today as they were then:

"What became of it?" asked the other, greatly interested.

"I don't know about that either," came the sad reply, "and I don't know anyone else who knows about the fate of the Cave Hill Diamond."

1. The Belfast Mountains circa 1810

The first version of this song was published as a ballad sheet in about 1810 by J. Catnach of Seven Dials, London. Its theme of unrequited love made it very popular and it was subsequently published on a ballad sheet by J. Pitts, also of Seven Dials, and again in chapbook form by P. Bucan of Peterhead. The melody is from George Petrie's *Ancient Music of Ireland* where it appeared, appropriately enough, under the title of *The Belfast Mountains*; it had been collected in 1859 from a P. MacDowell.

The Belfast Mountains

'Twas on the Belfast mountains
  I heard a maid complain,
Making a lamentation,
  Down by a purling stream,
She said I am confined,
  All in the bands of love,
All by a false pretender,
  That does inconstant prove.

O Johnny my dear jewel,
  Don't treat me with disdain,
Nor leave me here behind thee,
  In sorrow to complain.
His arms he clasped around me,
  Like violets round the vine,
This bonny Irish laddie,
  Has stole this heart of mine.

Had I but all the diamonds,
  That on the rocks do grow,
I'd give them to my Irish laddie,
  If he to me his love would show.
Wringing her hands and crying,
  O Johnny dear farewell,
To you Belfast mountains,
  My sorrows I will tell.

'Tis not those Belfast mountains,
　　Can give to me relief,
Nor is it in my power,
　　To ease me of my grief.
Had they but a tongue to prattle
　　Or tell me a loving tale,
To my bonny Irish laddie,
　　My mind I would reveal.

2. The Belfast Mountains
circa 1893

The second version of *The Belfast Mountains* was collected in 1893 by the well known English folk-song collector Lucy Broadwood from Henry Burstow, a shoemaker who lived in Horsham in Sussex. She collected the melody which was subsequently published by the English Folk Song Society. After eighty years the words are remarkably similar to the 1810 ballad sheet version but an extra stanza (verse three) has appeared in which the lover explains himself. A fine example of a song that has passed from the ballad sheet form into the mainstream folk-song repertoire.

The Belfast Mountains

All on the Belfast Mountains I heard a maid complain
Making forth her lamentation down by a purling stream
Saying my heart is fettered fast in the bonds of love
All by a false pretender who doth inconstant prove.

Oh Johnny, my dear jewel, don't treat me with disdain
Nor leave me here behind you in sorrow to complain
With her arms she clasps around him like violets round the vine
Saying my bonny Cheshire lad you've stole this heart of mine.

My dear I'm sorry for you that you for me should grieve
I am engaged already 'tis you I can't relieve
Since it is so my Johnny for ever I'm undone
All by this shame and scandal I shall distracted run.

If I'd but all those diamonds on yonder rock that grow
I would give them to my Cheshire lad if his love to me he'd show
Wringing her hands and crying my Johnny dear farewell
Unto those Belfast Mountains my sorrow I will tell.

It's not those Belfast Mountains can give to me relief
Nor is it in their power to ease me of my grief
If they'd but a tongue to prattle to tell my love a tale
Unto my bonny Cheshire lad my mind they would reveal.

3. The Belfast Mountains circa 1930

The third version of *The Belfast Mountains* was collected by Sam Henry in County Antrim in the 1930s along with several other versions. It was subsequently published in his "Songs of the People" column in the *Northern Constitution* together with its melody in tonic sol-fa form.

The text of this song has changed considerably from the 1810 Catnach version. The final verse is known as a floating verse because it appears in several other songs. The printed version refers to "the banks of Claudy" which appears in several other songs, but the location for Belfast should be the "banks of Clady"; the Clady River rises on the west slopes of Divis Mountain.

Sam Henry's unpublished versions of *The Belfast Mountains* are, however, remarkably similar to J. Catnach's version. A song can transcend time and place, travel orally and in the form of a ballad sheet yet still remain intact; such is the power of a thriving song tradition.

The Belfast Mountains

Being on the banks of Clady, I heard a maid complain,
Setting forth her lamentations down by yon purling stream,
Saying, "Here I lie confined in the constant bands of love,
All by a British sailor lad that did inconstant prove."

Chorus
It's O! you Belfast mountains, can you bring me no relief,
Have you got no tongue to flatter with, or to ease me of my grief?
Have you got no tongue to flatter with, or to ease me of my pain?
For it's hard to love an old sweetheart and not be loved again.

She twined her arms around my neck, just as we were going to part,
She twined her arms around my neck, saying "You're my old sweetheart."
She twined her arms around my neck, like the branches of yon vine,
Saying, "Jamie, cruel Jamie, you have broke this heart of mine."

Chorus

O! may you never prosper, nor may you never thrive,
In any job you take in hand as long as you're alive;
On the very ground whereon you stand may the grass refuse to grow,
For you're the whole occasion of my sad grief and woe.

Chorus

4. The Cavehill Diamond (1)

This song appeared on a ballad sheet published by J. Nicholson of 26 Church Lane, Belfast, who was one of the last printers of ballad sheets in business from about 1890 until 1918.

The song was written by a Professor Robert Hanna and dedicated to Lady Shaftesbury whose father, the third Marquis of Donegall, had built Belfast Castle on the slopes of Cavehill in 1870. He was obviously inspired by the much older ballad *Belfast Town*, from which he plagiarized the second and third verses. The legend of the Cavehill Diamond was nearly a hundred years old when he was writing the song.

The Cavehill Diamond

In Ireland's ancient days there lived a maid, the country's pride,
Whom many an honest youth adored, and strove to make his bride;
For she was modest, chaste, and good, of sweet and lovely fame,
She dwelt upon the Lagan side – Mary was her name.

Now Belfast City, so rich and large, was then a village small,
Flocks of sheep grazed on the spot where now stands the Linen Hall,
To herd the sheep was Mary's task, and she did ne'er repine,
She seemed so happy in her lot – she almost seemed divine.

Now about this time young Dermoid lived – the Royal Crown he wore;
He ruled the land from Belfast Lough to Mourne Mountains' shore,
To hunt the deer so savage wild was this young prince's pride,
By night or day he loved to stray upon the Cave Hill side.

A diamond bright, that shone by night, did often glitter there,
But Mary's eyes were brighter gems, thought Dermoid in despair,
And many a time did Dermoid think of these beauties rare,
The Cave Hill Diamond that shone so bright, or Mary that was so fair.

The time of year it did come on when lovers love to stray –
When primroses and blue-bells decorate the lea,
Round a nook by the Cave Hill Brook these lovers talked a while,
The Diamond bright it shone that night, and did their hours beguile.

"That Irish gem I love so well to wear it on my brow,
O Dermoid, love, by the stars above, will you procure it for me now?"
The maiden's request was hard to deny, the effort it was great,
The climb – the fall – the death – his scroll, was the young prince's fate.

The red-breast often bears a leaf upon their lonely graves,
When the Autumn's blast goes o'er Belfast, and moans through the
    Hill-of-Caves.
A fairy thorn it marks the spot where these lovers' fate was cast;
And Mary's memory is still held sweet by the lovely maidens of Belfast.

5. The Cavehill Diamond (2)

Sir Samuel Ferguson's historical romance *Corby Mac Gillmore*, published in 1887, was based on the fifteenth-century feuds between the Mac Gillmore clan and the Savages of the Ards. The Mac Gillmore's home was the large semi-circular hollow below the first cave on Cavehill, known as the Giant's Punchbowl. These feuds were inflamed when the only daughter of the Savages, Lady Mary, fell in love with Corby and fled with him to Cavehill to become his bride.

There are similar circumstances in this ballad. This time the feud is between the O'Neills of Lough Neagh and the Magennises of Dundrum. O'Neill's only daughter Eileen has fallen in love with Magennis but here the story differs and continues to a dramatic climax on Cavehill. The old ford of Belfast was where the rivers Lagan and Farset meet at the end of High Street opposite Skipper Street. It was here that silt and sand from the two rivers formed a sand bank that was to give Belfast its name – Béal Feirste, which means the mouth of the sand banks.

This song was printed on a ballad sheet from the presses of J. Nicholson, 26 Church Lane, Belfast.

The Cavehill Diamond

Oh! 'twas in the happy days of yore, ere Erin's prime had passed,
    And then as now the grey Cave Hill looked down on sweet Belfast,
Three caves its rugged bosom pierced, and one was as a cell,
    Used by a holy hermit who all lonely there did dwell.

From Bangor town to Antrim's glens far spread his holy fame,
    And pilgrims from both North and South to glean his wisdom came;
None knew his place of birth, and none his name or age could tell,
    But lint-white locks and snowy beard o'er his breast and shoulders fell.

Oh! grief and woe both dour and deep had long held dismal sway,
    Within the halls of bold O'Neill that looked o'er fair Lough Neagh,
For Princess Eileen, stern Red Hugh's sole child, had fled her home,
    And none could tell, tho' wide the search, where she did lonely roam.

In Dundrum's Castle, too, there's gloom, its walls no more resound,
    To minstrel's harp or Sennachies – no more the bowl goes round –
Its Chief, Magennis, tho' still young, and once so blythe and gay,
    Now mourns his love, the lost Eileen, the Lily of Lough Neagh.

For long they'd loved in secret, Dundrum's young chief and she,
    The only child of great O'Neill, sweet Eileen, bea-ma-chres[1]:
For deadly feud raged 'twixt the clans, Magennis and O'Neill,
    And fierce Red Hugh, with hardened heart, was deaf to all appeal.

Yet still they loved, and lived in hope, till Eileen, rent with grief,
    Was bid to wed the dread Earl James, Tyrconnell's aged chief,
'Twas then she fled her father's halls, Shane's ancient keep, and none
    From that sad day she left Lough Neagh could say where she had flown.

Three summer suns had shed their rays, three winters come and passed,
    Since Eileen on thy bosom fair Lough Neagh had gazed her last,
Dundrum's young chief still mourned his love, and hearing of the fame,
    Of Cave Hill's holy hermit, made a vow his aid to claim.

With trusty clansmen riding by down Lagan's side they passed,
    And crossed the placid river at the old ford of Belfast,
Along the strand the gallant band their winding way pursue,
    And just as sunset gilds the Lough the far-famed caves they view.

Next morn, betimes, rich gifts in hand, Magennis climbs the steep,
  To where the holy hermit does his lonely vigil keep;
Three times he winds his horn to make his presence duly known,
  Then mounts to where the Cave's dark mouth its shadows clear has thrown.

No sign the Hermit makes, the Cave yawns silent, black and grim,
  But naught can daunt Dundrum's young Chief, fear's all unknown to him,
With hasty step he passes o'er threshold, gazes round,
  And sees the aged Hermit lying prone upon the ground.

Without delay he passes in to aid the old Recluse,
  He lifts him gently from the ground and casts his mantle loose;
But see! what pales the young Chief's cheek, why troubles he so sore,
  The Hermit's snowy locks and beard are lying on the floor!

And in their place are tresses bright as strands of twisted gold,
  While to his own looks up a face he's known and loved of old;
With trembling hand the Hermit's garb he loosens to reveal,
  Clasped in his arms the fainting form of sweet Eileen O'Neill.

So young Magennis found his love, in spite of all disguise,
  And soon he's riding towards Dundrum with Eileen as his prize,
And as he rides he vows a vow his Bard shall well fulfil,
  To tell in song how he found his bride in the Hermit of Cave Hill.

So Cavehill provides the backdrop for many a romantic ballad but the same hill was a silent witness to a brutal murder that shocked Belfast on 12 March 1890 and was recalled in a ballad called *Nora's Grave:*

> 'Tis a tale of love and wild romance
> When Cupid dared to bend
> His mighty bow, and to fan the flame
> Of devouring love, when Nora came
> To her sad and tragic end.

On that day shots were heard from the direction of a lonely spot known as Lowry's Plantation. The bodies of two young people, Nora Tattersall and George Arthur, were discovered soon after. A revolver lay close by. Whether they shot themselves because they were prevented from marriage nobody knows but they were buried side by side in the city cemetery. The spot where they were found was marked with a pile of limestone and was known as Nora and Arthur's grave. Later this became Nora's grave and as the memory of the incident faded it became "Lovers' Lane".

> Let Nora sleep by her lover's side
> Nor their dreadful deed condemn
> For weak and frail is the human heart
> When Cupid wings his fiery dart
> The world was not for them.

BELFAST TOWN

Then was the times for games and gambles,
When Belfast Streets were covered with brambles,
Hedges and ditches and ponds of water,
But now there is nothing but bricks and mortar.

A New Song

Castle Place

The population of Belfast in 1800 was approximately twenty thousand but by 1900 it had risen to almost three hundred and fifty thousand. Between these two statistics lies the remarkable develop-ment of a quiet market town that became the thriving industrial city of Belfast. This meteoric expansion came under the scrutiny of numerous travellers who passed through the town on their Grand Tour of Ireland. Their descriptions were extensive and detailed; no facet of life escaped the critical eye of the stranger.

In 1806 Sir Richard Colt Hoare travelled from Antrim to Belfast over the White Mountains:

On descending this mountain Belfast soon opens; the fields white with linen, the country bespread by numerous manufactories; in short a commercial air enlivens the whole scenery.... It has some good streets, but no public buildings particularly worthy of remark.

J. Gamble stayed for a week in the town in 1813 and found much to divert him:

In the morning I walk the streets and frequent the libraries and in the evening I go to card parties and concerts. Music was the favourite recreation and many were no mean proficients in it.... Belfast concerts are never mere music meetings, they are always followed by a good supper and store of wine and punch.

In 1818 J.C. Curran recorded the sectarian struggles of the time:

A serious disturbance had recently taken place between the Orange party and the Roman Catholics.... Intolerance, with whatever colour it may deck itself, cannot serve, but may injure a good cause...

By now the industrial revolution was changing the face of Belfast. The rural tranquillity of the town was rapidly being eroded by the hum of industry. Mills and factories appeared at an incredible rate; it seemed as if every available pair of hands was being fully and usefully employed.

James Johnson wrote:

Voila Carrickfergus. From this to Belfast we are unequivocally in the land of long chimnies, white houses, and jet-black smoke with the Cavehill on our right and a large lough on our left. The scene altogether indicates wealth, industry and manufacture.

Another visitor to the town, Henry Inglis, was full of admiration for the industriousness of the Belfast worker:

The merchant of Cork is hunting while he of Belfast is at his desk and the tradesman of Dublin is in his jaunting car and entertaining company at his box at Kingstown while the tradesman of Belfast is minding his shop.

1841 saw the arrival of a very colourful character from America, a Mr N.P.Willis:

It was a market day at Belfast and the streets were thronged with the country people, the most inactive crowd of human beings, it struck me, that I had ever seen. The women were all crouching under their grey cloaks, or squatting upon the thills of the potato carts or upon steps or curb stones and the men were leaning where there was anything to lean against or dragging their feet heavily after them in a listless lounge along the pavement...

Mr Willis' sentiments aroused the fury of the inhabitants of Belfast as well as a visitor in the following year, William Makepeace Thackeray, who took great exception to the latter's deplorable descriptions:

These observations struck me as rather hard when applied to Belfast, which seemed to me really to be as neat, prosperous and handsome a city as need be seen.... It looks hearty, thriving and prosperous, as if it had money in its pockets and roast beef for dinner.... The houses are grave, stout red-brick edifices laid out at four angles in orderly streets and squares.

That same year Johann G. Kohl arrived from Germany and saw industrial Belfast by night:

Almost all the little towns through which we drove that evening were lit up with gas.... At length we arrived at the central point of all the gas lights in the North of Ireland... I thought at first that it must be some great festival for wherever I looked on every side I saw great houses, four, five and six stories high, illuminated from top to bottom. There were even buildings within which lights glittered from one hundred and two hundred windows. Yet all this was but the every-day or rather every-night appearance of a great manufacturing city.

Belfast continued to build its wealth and prosperity on its textile, engineering and shipbuilding industries. The goods produced gained a worldwide reputation for quality and reliability. In honour of all these achievements Belfast received a Royal Charter in 1888 from Queen Victoria and the town became a city. By the end of the nineteenth century the rapid expansion of industry and commerce had been thoroughly documented. New discoveries, such as electricity, were being made that would once again change the course of Belfast's history.

The following songs in their own way chart many facets of life throughout the nineteenth century, often with great humour and graphic detail. *The New Song* and *Gas Lights* describe town life in the early part of the century, contrasting with *His Lordship Had A Coachman* and *The Sights And Scenes Of Belfast* which paint a very different picture of town life towards the close of the century.

6. Gas Lights

In the 1980s Belfast witnessed the demise of a great public service which had begun over one hundred and sixty years ago. The *News Letter* of 2 September 1823 reported:

On the evening of the 30th ult. immense multitudes of people assembled to witness the lighting of our streets with gas and were highly gratified by the mild radiance flowing from the lamps.... The light now used is of the purest kind shedding on the streets a brilliant lustre – pleasing but not dazzling – and more resembling the clear effulgence of a cloudless atmosphere illuminated by the moon than any artificial beams heretofore produced by the imitative power of men.

The streets were suddenly transformed:

Living objects in our streets thus illuminated were distinctly seen, even at remote distances... each man could recognise his neighbour and the very shadows were well defined. We are pleased to find that... a passenger on the footway moves, as it were, in an alley of light and not a ray is lost in empty space.

The introduction of gas was hailed as "indubitable proofs of the rapid progress of science". The work of the labour force, who laid the pipes and built the gaswork's buildings, was highly praised:

It was, indeed, a common remark here that the labourers thus employed completed as much work in a week, as had usually been done in three, by the same number of hands.

It was a major step forward in the development of Belfast whose citizens had good reason for celebration.

This song was published in 1823.

Gas Lights

Ye poets that chooses ye bards and ye muses
Now lilt up a tune that is clever that's clever
Concerning Belfast and the new fashioned gas
That can from all darkness deliver deliver
To save all the poor an engine is in use
So great and so new and so dashing so dashing
That sweet furly fue that no mortal ever knew
Nor no Irishman saw such a fashion a fashion.

The heroes last season of wisdom and reason
Came over the same on to carry to carry
One Robson a neat man and Whowel a great man
And Spear that is famous and merry and merry
These jolly commanders are noble upstanders
To plan out the business so readily so readily
And each in his station with sweet moderation
Can rule his own share of this medley this medley.

Draw nigh all ye wonderers and view this fine congress
Of nature that joined in this valley this valley
From Scotland and England from Holland and Flanders
All meet with an Irish travally travally
Some hundreds of tall men of thick men and small men
Whose noise would scare home the auld devil the auld devil
They would raise a plearacha throughout the north walk
That would make all the wars grow civil grow civil.

The streets a-tearing a-splitting and sharing
While pavements laid waste in a-hurry a-hurry
Fine horses in traces to draw to their places
And hands that can shape dress and carry and carry
They work so complete with honour and state
The pride of the nation a-turning a-turning
The pipes they are placing like a new creation
With chipping and squaring and singing and singing.

There's work for the mason throughout the whole season
With lime wall square and true plummet true plummet
All building in state at this garden of Eden
The clouds near to reach at the summit the summit
The carpenters walls the best in their station
Fine pavers heaping up treasure up treasure
The sound of and all that's about this canal
They would raise a dead carline to pleasure to pleasure.

Last Saturday evening 'twas lively to see them
Career and carouse all together together
Without dread and fear the streets bright and clear
And good liquor to treat one another another
Each toasting his glass cries good luck to the gas
And long in Belfast may it tarry may't tarry
One cheer that is loud from the echoing crowd
And the Irishmen crying hadsarry hadsarry.

7. A New Song

One very important function of folk-song is social commentary whereby the man in the street can express his opinion without reservation or contradiction. The following song is a perfect example of this. The setting is Belfast in the 1820s. It is a critical time in the town's development. The familiar landscape of the village is rapidly being eroded by industrialisation. The population of Belfast in 1800 was about twenty thousand but by 1820 it had almost doubled to about thirty-eight thousand. The environs of Belfast, depicted as "covered with brambles, hedges and ditches and ponds of water", were being changed to such an extent that "now there is nothing but bricks and mortar". The quiet village life, in which "there was no sound heard but the small bird singing, except sometimes the village bell ringing", was fast disappearing to be replaced by multistorey mills and the incessant and pervasive noise of machinery.

No other song in the collection so graphically depicts the traumatic change from rural village to industrial town.

The first verse recalls the time when "ladies sides' were hooped like barrels." Hoops or hooped petticoats went out of fashion in the early 1800s to be replaced by controversial "body-clinging" dress designs.

The reference to the "Good old guinea" is to a King George III gold coin first minted in 1787. It was replaced in 1799 by a twenty shilling sovereign and later, in 1816, British silver coins were produced with an intrinsic value which was substantially below the face value. The year 1817 saw the introduction of Saint George slaying the dragon on the coins.

Pistol duelling took over in popularity from sword duelling in England in about 1770 and lasted until about about 1850. Duelling was practised in Ireland to such an extent that one of the most important and comprehensive codes of duelling for the English-speaking world was drawn up in Clonmel, County Tipperary, in 1777. Although there always had to be a surgeon or doctor on duty during a duel, the chances of getting wounded were generally fairly slim.

The New Marriage Act of 1823 stated that "All Banns of Matrimony shall be published in the parish church". It also laid down that "Before any such licence (of marriage) be granted, one of the parties shall personally swear before the surrogate or other person having authority to grant the same, that he or she believeth that there is no impediment of kindred or alliance... to bar or hinder the proceeding of the said matrimony." One of the most controversial requirements of the Act was "that such Banns shall not be published until the true Christian and Surnames of the said Persons and the House or Houses of their respective Abodes... shall be affixed on the principal Door of the Church or Chapel."

The first steam-driven mill in Ireland was built in Lisburn in 1789. By 1811 there were fifteen mills in and around Belfast using steam power. Steam engines were also being adapted for use in making paper and whiskey and minting coins.

Stricter controls on the strength and quality of alcoholic drinks were introduced in 1823.

The song was published in 1826 by Joseph Smyth of Belfast.

A New Song

I sing, I sing of good days older,
    When men and women were the bolder,
And when from Malt they brewed the Porter,
    When Lawyers were too wise for pillage,
And Belfast town was quite a Village,
    When Christmas times had Christmas Carols,
And ladies' sides were hooped like barrels.

Chorus
Sing hi sing ho, we can't but grieve,
    For the good old days of Adam and Eve.

When drinking Ale made strong men stronger,
    And Doctors made folks live the longer,
When our grandads brewed stout October,
    They thought it a sin to go to bed sober,
Then was the times for games and gambles,
    When Belfast Streets were covered with brambles,
Hedges and ditches and ponds of water,
    But now there is nothing but bricks and mortar.

When this very place now covered over,
  Was a field of wheat, perhaps of clover,
Two or three trees for the cattle to get under,
  Out of the road of the lightning and thunder,
There was no sound heard but the small birds singing,
  Except some times the village bells ringing,
But now those birds far away are fled sir,
  And we are the birds that sing instead sir.

When every man, whether wise or a ninny,
  Was pleased at the sight of a good old guinea,
The form of it had King George's face on,
  The Back had the arms and the old spade ace on,
But now our sovereigns I can tell you,
  They are not worth so much in value,
For there is St George without a rag on,
  Galloping over an ugly dragon.

When Lawyers, Clerks and Catgut scrapers,
  With their fists used to settle their quarrels and vapours,
They met like men, and first shook hands sir,
  Then pummelled each other while they could stand sir,
But now forsooth I pray you'd list all,
  To fight with sword or else with pistol,
A surgeon they have upon the ground sir,
  Yet the devil a man ever gets a wound sir.

When young men and women, they went a wooing,
  They always kept it to themselves what was a doing,
And wished to contrive their passion to smother,
  Quite unbecoming to their father and mother,
But now by the new marriage act so serious,
  It must be made known to all the parish,
Take affidavits, and what is more sir,
  They must have their names stuck on the Church door sir.

Now we have steam for boiling, steam for baking,
  Steam for printing and Sausage Making,
Steam to fire long balls and bullets,
  Steam for hatching young chickens and pullets,
The times are changed I do dream now,
  Everything does go by steam now,
In my young days, when I was little,
  There was no steam but from the kettle.

When young men and young women acted wise in
    Getting up to see the lark rising,
And could unless I am much mistaking,
    Eat for their breakfast, a pound of fat bacon.
But now our town and Parish gay sir,
    See Larks by night and not by day sir,
Gets into scraps and has long perrys[1],
    And to serve their backs on the floor the charleys[2].

Then we could get good wheat in measure,
    Then to spend our money it was a pleasure,
For three pence and that was not dear sir,
    You might have a quart of good strong beer,
But now what with pigeons craw and gall sir,
    Our beer is not fit to drink at all sir,
And since the Act is passed about the swipes[3] sir,
    What a devil of a number have the gripes sir.

    Sing hi sing ho, we can't but grieve,
        For the good old days of Adam and Eve.

8. The Sights And Scenes Of Belfast

A song that takes us on a tour of the city in the 1870s: the Docks, Smithfield and Berry Street, Pipe Lane Corner (now Winetavern Street), Donegall Street – where the Exchange was – Castle Street and High Street. At this time the bustle was in fashion and skirts could stand out from the waist by as much as sixteen inches; this style became known as the Grecian Bend. Also at that time the bun or chignon "tended to height and was decorated lavishly with flowers, feathers, lace or ribbons". Pipe Lane Corner, a colloquial name for Winetavern Street, derived from the local industry of clay pipe making, carried on by the Hamiltons from 1819 to 1931.

The tour of Belfast was not an unusual topic. In 1794 the *News Letter* reported on: "... a comic sketch called *Poor Darby's Trip To Belfast*. This sketch introduced comic ballads descriptive of the town, the public places, manners and fashions, etc. These were sung or recited by Mr. Cherry."

The Sights And Scenes Of Belfast

Good people all attention pay and listen for a while,
　　And if I cannot make you laugh I'm sure you'll have to smile,
It's of some curiosities that are constantly in view,
　　Of those who visit Belfast as the town they wander through.

So if you are really curious I would have you take a view,
　　Of the sights and scenes of Belfast as the town you go through.

The first thing I have to tell you I am but a country clown,
　　And to seek a situation I've just arrived in town,
I was born far from Ireland so I heard my daddy say,
　　At the thumb hand side, nor east one side of Hudson's Bay.

The moment that I landed the first thing that I espied,
　　Was the shipwreck of a handcart with the mud above its side,
I had to walk knee deep through it a job I did not like,
　　I was very near being swallowed up, the scavengers being on strike.

The fashions of the ladies they most certainly are droll,
　　They have things like tinkers' budgets[1] stuffed behind upon their poll[2],
And they wear an artificial hump upon their latter end,
　　That makes them look like dromedaries, it's called the Grecian Bend.

And if you pass by Smithfield and Berry Street all through,
　　You will see hawked linens and clothing both second-hand and new,
And if they find you're going to buy and then you've got tin,
　　You will have to be right careful or they'd tear you limb from limb.

Then pass by Pipe Lane Corner that place so clean and sweet,
　　And the potale[3] brigade you'll see on duty in the street,
And the lazy society about one hundred mixed,
　　All doing the Grecian Statues up against the bricks.

There's the lazy seat at the Exchange, that place of high renown,
    Where the laws for every nation and their people are laid down,
You will find among their congress a counter jumper[4] spruce,
    The waxy[5] with his lapstone[6] and the tailor with his goose[7].

All sorts of artful dodgers in Belfast you will meet,
    Going on with hunker sliding every night in Castle Street,
And if you go down farther in High Street you will find
    A fellow selling glasses to make blind men see behind.

Now there are other sights in Belfast that are nearly out of date,
    Which I would describe to you but 'twould take too long to wait,
But the next time that I see you I will surely have a line,
    On the Tramway, performing Fish, and the Easter pantomine.

9. His Lordship Had A Coachman

A fascinating song that takes us all around Belfast without going through a single street! I first heard the song from local singer and uilleann piper Trevor Stewart. I subsequently discovered from an article published in *Ireland's Saturday Night* on 26 March 1921 that the song was written by Fred Ginnet and performed by Juba the Clown. Ginnet's, like Hengler's and Cooke's, was a travelling circus which came annually to the site now occupied by the Grand Opera House and Cirque (to give it its full title). The song dates from 1888 when the Lord Mayor was Sir James Horner Haslett.

It is possible to do the circuit described in the song using street maps of the time, although some areas mentioned have now disappeared. For instance, Lagan Village was about half way up the Ravenhill Road and was famous for its potteries and glassworks. Lettuce Hill (now Hamill Street) once had thatched houses in the street. It was named after Lettice or Letitia Hincks, who was the third wife of the first Earl of Donegall. This fragment of an old ballad recalls the street:

> I walk on air around Smithfield
> And past the Brewery Mill
> To meet my lovely Eileen
> Who lives in Lettuce Hill.

His Lordship Had A Coachman

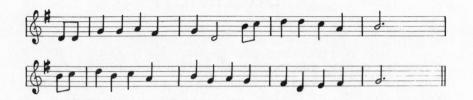

Now His Lordship had a coachman,
  And the coachman's name was John,
Said His Lordship to the coachman,
  "Take your wages and begone.

"For I want another coachman,
  As I'm going for a drive."
"Well," says John, "I'm the finest coachman sir,
  That you will find alive.

"Yes, and if you let me drive today,
  I'll show I can't be beat,
For I'll drive you all round Belfast town,
  And I won't go through a street."

Says His Lordship, "John, you must be mad,
  But still I'll humour you,
But remember that you lose your job,
  The first street you go through."

Well we started from the College,
  Yes, the College called the Queen's,
Up Rugby Road,
  Down Agincourt Avenue so green,

Ormeau Road, South Parade,
  Lagan Village too,
Short Strand, Donegall
  And the Queen's Quay we went through.

Now along the Docks to the New Road,
    The Station North we meet,
Says His Lordship, "John, I've got you now,
    You must take Canning Street."

"Oh no," says John, "that's not my way,
    I've got another mode,
Turn towards Carrickfergus Way,
    And up the Limestone Road.

"Now we're turning to the left –
    Atlantic Avenue,
Then the Antrim Road we gently trot,
    Till the Bag of Meal's in view,

"The county jail means Crumlin Road,
    Then the Old Lodge we will drive."
And so to keep out of a street,
    John artfully contrives.

From Peter's Hill to Millfield –
    Says His Lordship in a fit,
"Oh dash my wig and spectacles,
    By God, you'll do it yet."

Lettuce Hill and King Street Mews,
    (Says John, "that's not a street")
Fisherwick and Glengall Place,
    Are the places next we meet.

Says His Lordship, "John, I've got you now,
    Great Victoria Street I know,"
But John went through the station yard,
    And into Sandy Row.

From there to the square called Shaftesbury,
    Then Botanic Avenue,
Down the Avenue we trot along,
    Till the College is in view.

"Well," says John, "I've got you done,
    I think you've had a treat,
For I've driven you round Belfast town
    And never touched a street."

COTTON AND LINEN

But the time is drawing nigh when the shuttle will fly
And no more idle hands to be seen.

The Ports Are Open

Roughing, York Street Mill

Her merchants are honoured throughout the world
The sails of her ships in all parts are unfurled
In science her college takes a proud stand
Diffusing intelligence over the land.
Then let us all strive to make Ireland our boast
As free as the billows that break on her coast
And still may this motto be nailed to the mast
Success to the Town and the Trade of Belfast.

Then here's to "old Ireland" the land we love best
And dear "Northern Athens" the pride of the West
Prosperity beams on her, long may it last –
Success to the Town and the Trade of Belfast.

Success to Belfast was written by a prominent Belfast man, T.C.S. Corry, and published in *Irish Lyrics, Songs and Poems* in 1879. Later it was printed as a broadside ballad and thousands of copies were sold; in the short space of a verse and chorus the song had encapsulated the buoyant mood of the time. Trade in the linen industry had never been better. Business was booming and Belfast had become renowned world wide as a centre of industry and commerce. The linen industry had transformed a market town into a prosperous commercial town, but the rapid industrial expansion and wealth in Belfast was not solely due to the linen industry.

In 1778 cotton spinning was introduced into the Poor House in Clifton Street, Belfast, so that the children could be usefully employed. From this small beginning a major industry developed. By 1790 cotton mills were using machinery powered by steam for spinning and by early 1800 cotton spinning had become the chief industry in Belfast. The industry was at its height in the mid-1820s and by the end of the decade it was in decline, mainly due to the lifting of trade tariffs in 1824, which had until then protected the Irish cotton trade from fierce competition from Britain.

Ironically, the demise of the cotton industry brought a new lease of life to the linen industry. The technical expertise and wealth generated by the cotton trade was channelled into new technology and machinery for the manufacture and sale of linen, a modernisation which was long overdue. Even in 1821 linen yarn was still being spun by hand on spinning wheels in farmhouses and cottages, but all that was soon to change. A new process of spinning flax using a wet process was being developed in England and a local mill owner, Thomas Mulholland, saw what immense benefits could be gained by introducing this system into Belfast. Locally grown flax was already being exported to England for mechanised wet spinning and brought back again for weaving. He wanted home-grown flax to be spun locally and there was the added attraction that yarn spun by machine was much superior in quality to hand-spun yarn. However, most mill and factory owners were slow to introduce new-fangled machinery because there was such a large pool of cheap labour to draw on. It was a simple economic fact that the employers could pay low wages instead of investing large sums in new machinery. But after the famine years of the 1840s, large-scale emigration caused a drain of skilled labour and labour costs spiralled rapidly. By 1850 power looms were introduced in the linen industry for weaving.

In 1861 the start of the American Civil War dealt another blow to the ailing cotton industry. Supplies of raw cotton were halted and while cotton products almost disappeared, demand for linen products rocketed. Between 1862 and 1868 the number of power looms increased from three thousand to nine thousand and seven new weaving factories opened. Investment increased with demand; it was a time of great wealth and profit. By 1873 the linen industry in Belfast was recognised as the largest centre of production in the world.

During the last quarter of the century, linen was Belfast's only major industry, as the cotton industry was almost extinct, and by the end of the century both industries were facing stiff competition from developing overseas markets. Belfast, however, was gaining a worldwide reputation in another sphere – shipbuilding. A new era of economic prosperity was looming and it was still a case of

Prosperity beams on her, long may it last –
Success to the Town and the Trade of Belfast.

10. Campbell's Mill

"Quitting Belfast in a SW direction the only objects in the suburbs worthy of notice are... a large cotton mill belonging to Messrs Boomer and Campbell..." wrote Philip Dixon Hardy in *The Northern Tourist* (1830). The mill was situated in Bath Place, which was a small area sandwiched between the present Townsend Street and Boundary Street, although these streets were not then in existence. Known locally as Campbell's Mill, it was the last building on the town side of Belfast and beyond was open countryside. It changed ownership several times during the nineteenth century and also changed from cotton spinning to flax spinning; it finally ceased trading as the Irish Flax Spinning Co. Ltd in about 1920.

The song is set appropriately enough within walking distance of the mill. Castle Street is today a thriving business area, while Carrick Hill or "The Hill" is now Upper Library Street. It was part of the main thoroughfare through Belfast, which went from Carrickfergus Street (now North Queen Street) to Millfield, Barrack Street, Sandy Row and on to Malone Road. It is hard to believe that such a relatively quiet area as Upper Library Street was once a bustle of activity. It was a warren of small streets, courts and entries where publicans, grocers, tinsmiths, cart makers, glassmakers, weavers and other small traders eked out an existence.

It makes a welcome change in a traditional song that not only does the girl rebuff the advances of this "fine well looking gentleman" for her lover's sake, but also because she has the security of a trade.

Campbell's Mill

As I roved out the other day
When I had nothing else to do
While walking down through Castle Street
A lovely maid came in my view.

She had a nice pink cotton gown
Bound with a light blue frill
That moment Cupid stung my heart
With the maid who works in Campbell's Mill.

Said I fair maid what is your name
Be pleased to let me know
Do you stray far along this way
For along with you I'd like to go.

My name to you sir I won't tell
But I reside in Carrick Hill
A man like you what would you do
With a girl that works in Campbell's Mill.

Your enchanting looks have won my heart
One look of you is fit to kill
So come with me no more to roam
So early to the spinning mill.

Oh no kind sir I'll mind my trade
And I would have you understand
That I'm no equal match for you
A fine well looking gentleman.

And I gave my hand to a young man
Whose charms to me my bosom fills
He's a heckler[1] lad and my delight
And he works with me in Campbell's Mill.

So fare ye well I must away
For the last whistle said its will
I must go back to my young man
Who works with me in Campbell's Mill.

11. The Cotton Mill Song

The mill referred to in this song is probably the Springfield Cotton Mill built by Stevenson and Company in 1805, one of the earliest large-scale mills in Ulster and the last cotton spinning mill in Ireland when it closed in 1919. It was situated in Springfield Village (now the Springfield Road end of Woodvale Avenue), which was specifically constructed for the mill workers. Both mill and houses were built with the same dark-coloured stone and not the red brick normally associated with mills.

The song embodies an unusual juxtaposition of urban and rural environments. Belfast in the early 1800s was on the threshold of an industrial revolution which was to transform the town and its environs. Pockets of mill villages were appearing on the surrounding hillsides, lured there by free water-power generated by the rivers and tributaries cascading down the hill. Peaceful countryside was being disturbed by the new sounds of industry and Springfield Village was no exception.

The picture of pleasant countryside portrayed in the song by the lines "We strolled along the dam..." and "the birds were singing sweetly..." belies the gruelling work and long hours spent in the mill. The song dwells on the contentment of a couple whose whole existence depended on the mill, and whose children were to be reared to work there also. It is a product of a generation caught up in nineteenth-century industrial growth and prosperity.

The Cotton Mill Song

I took my love out for a walk in the merry month of May
The birds were singing sweetly as we went along the way
She said she loved me dearly and to me she would prove true
If you will stay with me my love, sure I will stay with you.

Chorus
We strolled along the dam and the birds sang loud and gay
It was there I met my pretty brunette and she stole my heart away
Her cheeks they were like roses red and her skin as white as snow
She is the darling of my heart and the pride of the Springfield Road.

Well now we are to marry for she has named the day
And happy we'll be together as we go all on our way
We'll have a tidy little house and a garden for to till
And we'll bring the children up like us to work in the Cotton Mill.

Chorus

Well I'll bid you all good evening to her parents I must go
To see if they will have me now or if the answer's no
She says they'll treat me kindly and my glass they'll surely fill
And they'll drink a toast to the bride and groom that work in the
     Cotton Mill.

Chorus

12. Young McCance

The country in this direction (south west), onwards along the foot and side of the mountain presents a scene of the most pleasing and gratifying description – numerous extensive bleach greens with the houses and finely planted demesnes of the wealthy proprietors. The green of John Sinclair Esq. first presents itself and, a little further on, that of William McCance Esq. On the right hand side of the road stands the private residence of the latter gentleman, an elegant though plain building with handsome pleasure grounds... In ascending the hill to the left appears the magnificent mansion of John McCance Esq. of Suffolk – the most splendid, perhaps, belonging to any man of business in the kingdom.

So wrote Philip Dixon Hardy in his book *The Northern Tourist* published in 1830.

John McCance, the owner of this splendid mansion, was born in 1772 and lived until 1835. In partnership with his cousin John Stroupe he bleached linen at Granville on the slopes of Colin Mountain. He also inherited another bleach green and linen business from his uncle William McCance of Upper Falls and Ballycullo. At the age of twenty-nine John McCance became a magistrate and in 1821 he joined the private bank of Orr, Sloan, McCance and Montgomery, which three years later became the Northern Bank. The following year he became High Sheriff of County Down and in 1827 he was made High Sheriff of County Antrim. In the year of his death he became MP for Belfast. He had a great interest in sport and had two horses – Mayboy and Navarino – which regularly ran at the Maze and Derry racecourses; he also kept a pack of hounds for hunting.

The song is correct in mentioning McCance's dwelling at the foot of Divis Mountain: he lived at Roselands on the Upper Falls before moving to Suffolk House in 1811. The "purling stream" is the Colin River, which ran through his father's land at Farmhill (now in the Black's Road area). Colin Glen was at one time known as McCance's Glen, and before that as The Rumbling Hole.

Young McCance

At the foot of Divis mountain
    My dwelling is to be seen
Where there runs a purling stream
    Beside my father's green,
Well covered o'er with linen cloth
    Which was wrought round Tandragee[1]
And purchased by young McCance,
    And a boy called Darby Gray.

As I walked out one morning
    To view my father's men
The Armagh coach[2] came rolling in
    Well loaded to the ground;
I put my spy-glass to my eye
    And viewed her round and round,
And on the front seat of the coach
    Sat a damsel of renown.

I then did follow after
    To help her from the coach;
I took her by the milk-white hand
    And led her round the beach,
All for to view my father's ships,
    Which were bound for Chester fair;
Had it not been for your beauty,
    My dear, I might have been there.

We did not proceed much farther
    Until I asked her in,
All for to take a glass of wine,
    Our courtship to begin;
Said I, – I lost a diamond
    More precious than the gold,
And you are the one that found it,
    Fair lady, I am told.

I am no honoured lady,
    Altho' I wear fine clothes;
To keep company with a gentleman,
    I never will propose;
I am but a farmer's daughter
    That has come from Hamilton's Ban,
And for farther information,
    Sir, I dwell in Drummond's Land.

Says I, – My handsome fair one,
    If you and I agree,
We shall take the Armagh coach
    And Drummond's Land we'll see;
Five hundred pounds in ready gold
    On your father I will bestow,
And I'll crown you Queen of Drummond's Land
    This night before I go.

She says, Kind Sir, I am sorry,
    That your suit must be denyed;
I have a true-love of my own,
    And he will make me his bride;
I have a true-love of my own,
    Has love for me in store;
He is but a linen weaver,
    But the boy that I adore.

As I walked out that evening,
    Down through my father's land,
Was not I a clever fellow,
    With my fusee[3] in my hand;
I might have had sweethearts plenty,
    Had I but knew my fate;
I am young McCance, I am from the Falls,
    You know my fortune is great.

13. You Might Easy Know A Doffer

The making of linen involved many different processes and numerous trades. Tenters, winders, hecklers, rovers, band-tiers, spinners and weavers all had their places in the manufacture of linen. Inevitably there was rivalry and snobbery among the workers.

I'll give a curse to any girl who wants to be a spinner.

Never marry a reeler
For you wouldn't know her pay
But marry a good old spinner
With her belly wet all day.

But the hecklers are of the best class.

The song reflects the animosity which existed between doffers and weavers and expresses the doffers' point of view. The tools of the doffer were pickers, a scraper, hackle pins and whistle; these were tied around her waist on a piece of string.

You Might Easy Know A Doffer

You might easy know a doffer
When she comes into town
With her long yellow hair
And her pickers[1] hanging down
With her rubber[2] tied before her
And her scraper[3] in her hand
You might easy know a doffer
For she'll always get a man
    Oh she'll always get a man
    Oh she'll always get a man
    You might easy know a doffer
    For she'll always get a man

You might easy know a weaver
When she comes into town
With her old greasy hair
And her scissors[4] hanging down
With a shawl[5] around her shoulders
And a shuttle[6] in her hand
You will easy know a weaver
For she'll never get a man
    No she'll never get a man
    No she'll never get a man
    You will easy know a weaver
    For she'll never get a man

14. The Doffing Mistress

Machines were used in the spinning room to spin linen yarn onto empty bobbins on a frame. When they were full the doffers had to "doff" or remove the bobbins and replace them with empty ones. All this work was carried out under the supervision of the doffing mistress, who could be a very popular person or the subject of vicious ridicule.

Inevitably during spinning the fine yarn frequently snapped and the two loose ends had to be tied together or "laid up" again so that spinning could continue, hence the expression "lay up your ends".

Only a few songs about the linen industry have survived, and this is by far the most popular. It is well known throughout the northern countryside as well as in England. There are other variations of the song in which the name of the doffing mistress changes. The song portrays a lot of human emotions: the resentment felt towards the new doffing mistress who not only hangs her coat on the highest frame but bosses them all on Monday mornings; defiance and sarcasm, and sadness at parting. All these sentiments are harnessed to a stirring melody ensuring the abiding popularity of the song.

The Doffing Mistress

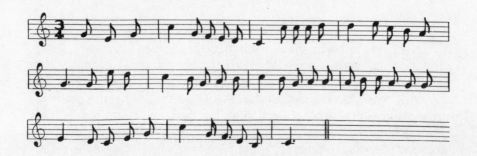

Oh do you know her or do you not?
This new doffing mistress that we have got,
Oh Agnes Savage it is her name,
And she hangs her coat upon the highest frame.
Ra-de-ri-fle-ra, ra-de-ri-fle-ree.

On Monday morning when she comes in
She hangs her coat upon the highest pin,
She turns around for to view her girls,
Saying, "Damn you doffers, lay up your ends."
Ra-de-ri-fle-ra, ra-de-ri-fle-ree.

"Lay up our ends we will surely do,
Our hands are steady and our touch is true,
Lay up our ends we will surely do,
All for Lizzie Murphy but not for you."
Ra-de-ri-fle-ra, ra-de-ri-fle-ree.

"Oh Lizzie Murphy, now you're going away,
It is every night that for you we'll pray,
You've left us here with a broken heart,
For there's no one left that will take our part."
Ra-de-ri-fle-ra, ra-de-ri-fle-ree.

HORSE TRAMS

Do you mind the old horse trams a long time ago
As they passed through the city at jog-trot or slow?

A Trace-Boy On Ligoniel Hill

High Street, Belfast

At half-past one o'clock yesterday the first section of the Belfast Tramway system was opened... and the opinion was unanimous that an immense stride has been made in our local means of locomotion.

That was how the *Northern Whig* reported the advent of the horse tram system on 28 August 1872. Belfast had moved gracefully into a new era of transport with the Belfast Street Tramway Company. The fleet consisted of three single-decker cabs, each drawn by one horse. The horses were stabled at Wellington Court and the cabs were parked along Wellington Place. The first route was from Castle Place via Donegall Place, Donegall Square North, Wellington Place, Great Victoria Street, University Road to Botanic Gardens. The fare for this journey was 2d.

This, however, was not the first public transport in Belfast. Trains had been in operation since 1839 and jaunting-cars, chariots, landaus, private carriages, gigs, sedan chairs and the horse-omnibuses were available to those who could afford them. It was the horse-omnibuses that developed as a viable form of public transport in the city. When Great Victoria Street railway station opened in 1849 a service was run by the Railway Omnibus Company from Malone Road to the town centre. Many hotel proprietors ran services on a small scale transporting their patrons from their hotels to the railway stations. By 1870 there were three rival horse-omnibus companies – Boyd's, Walker's and the Express Bus Company – with routes extending to Carlisle Circus, Cavehill Road, Fortwilliam, Sydenham, Newtownbreda and Milltown Cemetery. Often routes overlapped and competition became so fierce that price-cutting was introduced to increase the number of passengers. The Express Bus Company had a novel idea to ensure that passengers travelling at night were in no doubt as to which company they were with. They proudly announced:

To prevent confusion, our cars on the Antrim Road at night will have red curtains and red lights and our Northern Counties Railway Cars will have blue curtains and blue lights.

Horse-omnibuses, however, were no match for horse trams that ran on specially laid metal track. A journey in such a horse tram was much smoother, faster and quieter than that in a horse-omnibus jolting its way through cobbled streets. Less effort was required for a horse to pull a tram, and so more passengers per horse could be transported. In 1881 double-deckers, drawn by two horses, were introduced together with a flat fare of 2d. for a journey anywhere in the town. With an ever-expanding tramway system and cheaper fares horse-omnibuses could not compete and finally disappeared in 1892.

Between 1871 and 1891 the population in Belfast had increased by ninety-nine thousand. During the same period housing stock quadrupled to cater for increased demand. The city boundary was pushing out in all directions and the horse tram system developed new routes. By 1873 the system had extended to York Street via Donegall Street to Ormeau Road via Cromac Street to Ormeau Bridge. By 1881 it was over the Queen's Bridge to County Down to Mountpottinger and the Albertbridge Road, out to Windsor on the Lisburn Road and to Chichester Park on the Antrim Road. By 1892 it extended to Stranmillis, Malone, Newtownards Road, Cliftonville, Grosvenor Road, Springfield and out the Lisburn Road as far as Balmoral. By 1900 it was going up Bedford Street to Ballynafeigh on the Ormeau Road, up the Falls and to Crumlin, Ligoniel and Belmont.

Conditions for passengers improved. Upstairs the standard knife-edged seat, which was a double-sided bench running down the middle of the tram, was replaced with rows of garden seats. This innovation was copied by other companies in England. Access to the top was by way of rickety iron ladders and these were replaced by spiral staircases. Sunday trams were introduced and not without protest from some church leaders who accused the authorities of committing a sin by forcing their officials to work on Sundays.

In 1896 an Act of Parliament authorised the Company to install electric trams. Electric trams were in operation in Dublin from 1896 and in Cork from 1898, but it wasn't until Tuesday 5 December 1905 that the first electric tram line was officially opened with great pomp and ceremony in Belfast. On the same day the last horse tram ambled quietly and unceremoniously back to the depot.

The press that had hailed the horse tram system as "an immense stride" in 1872, thirty-three years later had grown weary of the system: "It has lagged superfluous on the scene for the last five years". Two weeks later a selection of horses and tram-cars was sold off at a public auction in the Royal Ulster Agricultural Society premises at Balmoral. The remaining tram-cars were converted for use on the electric tramway system and some remained in operation until 1939.

15. The New Tramway

By the summer of 1873 the tramway system had been extended to Carlisle Circus via Bridge Street and Donegall Street. This song dates from that time since the lady referred to in the first verse is seen in High Street looking out of her window with obvious curiosity at a passing tram. Apart from the amorous adventure on the tram the song captures the excitement and the novelty of a journey in a tram. It remained very popular and was sung with slightly different words at a dinner for the drivers and conductors in the Ulster Hall on 16 January 1894:

> Riding on the tramway smoking a cigar,
> Flirting with a pretty girl heedless of her Pa...

It is obvious from the catchy melody combined with the topical content of the words that this was a song from the music halls which found its way into the mainstream traditional song repertoire.

The New Tramway

I have a tale to tell you, I'll give you all to know,
   I lodged up in Ann Street a night or two ago;
As I walked up through High Street, I saw a lady gay
   Looking out of a window at the New Tramway.

Chorus
Riding on the Tramway that's the game for me,
Riding on the Tramway, happy, gay and free.
The sum is only two pence that you have to pay
To do the hurdy gurdy on the New Tramway.

I held up my finger and the car did quickly stop,
   I had not long been standing there when inside I did pop;
I hardly had got seated when I heard a lady say,
   It's folly to be riding on the New Tramway.

Chorus

I asked her would she marry me upon next Sunday morn,
   I could no longer tarry as I felt quite forlorn;
Oh, yes, says she, I'll marry thee, and be happy all the day;
   I kissed her, and I hugged her on the New Tramway.

Chorus

I married her, I do declare, and made her my dear wife,
    I often thought how nice it was to have a charming life;
She says she loves me dearly, believe me when I say,
    We'll soon have fresh conductors on the New Tramway.

Chorus

This job being fairly over the truth, I will declare
    You will not rue the cost when you have paid your fare
I mean to end my ditty, I have no more to say,
    I hope you all may give a call on the New Tramway.

Chorus

16. A Trace-Boy On Ligoniel Hill

As the tramway network followed the rapidly expanding city out to the encircling hills an increasing problem was the difficulty of two horses pulling a double-decker full of passengers up the steep inclines. But the problem was solved by hitching two extra horses onto the team using traces. This task was done by trace-boys who waited at the bottom of steep hills such as Ligoniel or at the corner of Beechmount Avenue on the Falls Road. The Ligoniel Tramway system started up in the summer of 1885.

The reference to "my bed a brick kiln" is a reminder of the days when Belfast had many brick manufacturing companies. After a day's firing the kilns retained their heat for a considerable time so that many tramps and paupers took advantage of the free heat for the night.

A Trace-Boy On Ligoniel Hill

Do ye mind the old horse trams a long time ago
As they passed through the city at jog-trot or slow?
On the level they cantered, but the pace it did kill,
When they got to the bottom of Ligoniel Hill.

But the trace-boys were there with a heart and a hand
They let down the traces and buckled each band,
The passengers sat on contented and still,
When they saw the bold trace-boys of Ligoniel Hill.

Away we did canter as fast as the wind
And left the poor country carts plodding behind;
And that song of the wind in my ears I hear still,
As when I was a trace-boy on Ligoniel Hill.

The youth of today hold their heads in the air,
And the young girls pass by with a golliwog stare,
Let them pity the crulge[1] in my back if they will
But I once was a trace-boy on Ligoniel Hill.

My friends all departed, and work now so scarce,
The only thing left is a ride in a hearse,
For the sky is my roof and my bed a brick-kiln,
Yet I once was a trace-boy on Ligoniel Hill.

17. The Belfast Tram

The enthusiastic public response to the introduction of horse trams soon gave way to constant complaints about their lack of punctuality. The problem was that no timetable was published other than a general directive that trams would run at ten minute intervals. On 3 December 1872 the *Northern Whig* commented:

The new cars seem to enjoy great popularity and are still objects of curiosity. For the present no attempt seems to be made at punctuality but it is perhaps too soon yet to expect this. When a larger section is opened and when matters have got into smooth working order a punctual system of running from stated points will be so essential to the property of tramways that the company are sure to adopt it. People must be able to depend on getting the cars out and in at least as regularly as the old omnibuses and more frequently or they will not come to regard them as reliable means of locomotion.

Mr Larsen, Managing Director of the Belfast Street Tramway Company, offered a wonderful defence of his company's policy:

While the affair is in this experimental stage the company are unwilling to fetter their freedom of action by publishing a timetable which might soon prove to be inconvenient both for the public and themselves.

Public opinion was not assuaged and the following song is certainly very scathing about the reliability and the punctuality of the trams. The Belmont tramway line referred to was constructed by Sydenham District Tramways and later leased to the Belfast Street Tramway Company in 1885.

Again this song is in the music hall mould and was published in *Ireland's Saturday Night*.

The Belfast Tram

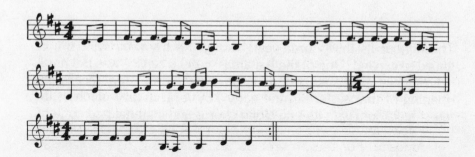

Chorus
There's a vehicle on wheels they call a Belfast Tram
It should "Save your soles" and heels should the Belfast Tram
But you wait and wait in vain standing shiv'ring in the rain
If you want to be late again take a Belfast Tram

If you wish to catch a train avoid a Belfast Tram
Better use your "Shanks" again than a Belfast Tram
Take a taxi or sidecar "Hitch your waggon to a star"
Or else stay where you are and "Bless" the Belfast Tram

Chorus

If you wish to "Call on sorrow" take a Belfast Tram
You will catch it "some" tomorrow in a Belfast Tram
If a friend you'd rather miss, says he'll call, then think of this
In his ear gently hiss – "Take a 'Belmont' Tram"

Chorus

Oh the things we'd like to say about the Belfast Trams
But we will not though we may about the Belfast Trams
We can only wait and pray for the coming "Perfect Day"
When we get the length we pay for on the Belfast Trams

Chorus

18. The Tramway Line

Throughout its thirty-three-year history the tramway system continued to expand. One of the last areas to get a service was Balmoral.

Originally published on a ballad sheet, this song recalls the opening of that system in the early 1890s. It is very much in the music hall idiom with its sing-along chorus and light-hearted content.

The Tramway Line

Kind gents list with polite attention
   Pray listen to my song
About the work that's in Belfast
   That's going on so strong
The men are toiling night and day
   To get it done in time
Till the people get a penny trip
   Upon the Tramway Line.

Chorus
Pipe it, twig it, it is a gorgeous show
   Here and there and everywhere
It's through the streets they go.
   Red Roger he's to be a guard
In a box he'll sit behind
   To keep people from falling out
Upon the Tramway Line.

It was on the eighth of August
    That every one does know
Lord Lurgan and Lord Lieutenant
    Went to the Cattle Show
They walked about and indulged themselves
    Till they felt inclined to dine
And they took a bird's-eye view
    Upon the Tramway Line.

Chorus

There is a girl in Belfast
    In Ann Street she does dwell
She wears a hat and a feather
    And cuts a pretty swell
She says she knows Red Roger
    And she will speak in time
That she may get a ticket
    Upon the Tramway Line.

Chorus

CHILDREN'S SONGS

Boys and girls come out to play
The moon doth shine as bright as day
Come with a whoop, come with a call
Come with goodwill, or don't come at all
Lose your supper and lose your sleep
So come to your playmates in the street.

The Dancing Master

Children playing Churchie

It may come as a surprise to some people to discover that *I'll Tell Me Ma* is not a local song peculiar just to Belfast, but a version of a song which also exists in Britain and America. It illustrates the fact that children's street games as we know them are part of a universal folklore and of a self-perpetuating oral tradition that has survived to this day without adult intrusion. Versions of *Jenny Jo,* for example, may be found in Britain, America, Australia, Spain and even Russia.

In some ways it is hardly surprising that this is so, since children's fertile imaginations know no boundaries. It is their inherent ability to mimic and become whatever they want to become, whether it is an aeroplane, tree, animal or whatever. Through street games they are constantly acting out the cycle of birth ("The wife wants a child..."); courtship ("Here is one knight has come from Spain, a-courting of your daughter Jane..."); marriage ("Now they are married, life enjoy..."); and death ("Poor Toby is dead and lies in his grave..."). These games catered for many age groups and they were always executed with great ritualistic endeavour and emotion more akin to the adult world.

Many of these street games have disappeared, though some are still played. Children now have many alternative attractions vying for their attention – television being the principal one. It stimulates their imaginations in different ways, giving them a wider range of role models to imitate, and they prefer the glitter and razzmatazz of television and cinema. From an early age their leisure time is programmed by the whim and hype of the media. The era of streets thronged with children entertaining themselves singing and playing their age-old street games has long since passed.

19. Here's A Poor Widow From Sandy Row

Here's a poor widow from Sandy Row
With all her children behind her
One can knit and one can sew
And one can make a winder go
Please take one in, please take one in.

Now poor (Nellie) she is gone
Without a farthing in her hand
Nothing but a guinea gold ring
Goodbye (Nellie) goodbye

In this game two of the bigger girls are chosen, one to represent the Widow and the other the Lady. The Lady takes her place at the outset, while the remaining players arrange themselves on either side of the Widow, with whom they advance and retire hand in hand while they sing. At "Please take one in" the Lady chooses one girl from the line and the song then continues with the children advancing and retiring as before to the end when the Widow and the girl chosen shake hands. The game goes on until all the girls have been take over by the Lady.

This is a variation of an English singing game known as "The Lady of the Land". The reference to "make a winder go" dates back to handlooms when the younger members in a family were allocated the task of winding yarn onto the bobbins for the weaver's shuttle.

20. Jenny Jo

The children form themselves into two parties. The first consists of Jenny with her father and mother. Jenny, who is normally a very small child, is concealed behind her parents. All the other children form the party of suitors. The visiting party retire a short distance away and then approach Jenny's house singing:

> We've come to court Jenny Jo
> Jenny Jo, Jenny Jo
> We've come to court Jenny Jo
> Is she within?

Something tragic has happened but the parents wish to temporise so they sing in reply:

> Jenny Jo's washing clothes
> Washing clothes, washing clothes
> Jenny Jo's washing clothes
> Can't see her today.

The visiting party who are holding hands retire slowly, walking backwards while they sing:

> Then fare ye well ladies o
> Ladies o, Ladies o
> Then fare ye well ladies
> And gentlemen too.

The visiting party return immediately singing as before and this is repeated several times. Each time they receive an excuse that Jenny is "drying clothes", "starching clothes", "ironing clothes", until at long last the afflicted parents are forced to announce the sad news that:

> Jenny Jo's lying dead
> Lying dead, lying dead
> Jenny Jo's lying dead
> You can't see her today.

They all add:

> So turn again ladies o
> Ladies o, Ladies o
> So turn again ladies
> And gentlemen too.

But instead of returning to their homes the party remain and sing:

> What shall we dress her in
> Dress her in, dress her in
> What shall we dress her in
> Shall it be red?

Then the unhappy parents answer:

> Red's for the soldiers
> The soldiers, the soldiers
> Red's for the soldiers
> And that will not do.

Various other colours are suggested in song but all are found unsuitable: black, because "black's for the mourners"; green because "green's for the croppies"; orange, because "orange is for the orangemen", and so on until white is suggested and the parents sing:

> White's for the dead people
> The dead people, the dead people
> White's for the dead people
> And that will just do.

The parents then step aside to reveal Jenny lying perfectly still. A hush falls on the little party. A funeral has to be arranged when suddenly Jenny Jo springs to life again and the game finishes with wild rejoicings.

This song was published in *Notes and Queries* on 19 December 1891. It was sent by W.H. Patterson of Belfast in answer to a request by A.B. Gomme for street games. W.H. Patterson recalled:

It was very pleasant to see the graceful figures of the little children, many of them bare-footed, advancing and retiring, their steps keeping time to the very simple pretty air to which they sang their rhymes and which comes back to me after many years. Owing to the amount of repetition the performance lasted a long time – that is, a long time for a game played by young children – but the dramatic character of it no doubt kept up their interest and in the long fine summer evenings it was repeated many times by many little parties of young performers.

21. Round About The Punchbowl

Singing *Round About The Punchbowl* the players join hands to form a ring. They dance around and sing the verse. At the words "one, two, three," all the players drop down to a crouching position for a few seconds. If anybody falls they have to leave the ring and the game continues until all the players fall.

> Round about the punch bowl, punch bowl, punch bowl
> Round about the punch bowl, one, two, three.
>
> First time never to fall, never to fall, never to fall,
> First time never to fall, one, two, three.
>
> Second time catching time, catching time, catching time,
> Second time catching time, one, two, three.
>
> Third time kissing time, kissing time, kissing time,
> Third time kissing time, one, two, three.

Another game with the same name was collected by Clara M. Patterson at Ballymiscaw Primary School in the 1890s:

> Round about the punchbowl, once, twice, three
> The last time they catch in time, they'll not catch me
> (Lizzie) made a pudding so nice and so sweet
> Saying taste, love, taste, love, don't say nay
> For next Sunday morning to church we will go
> Rings on her fingers and bells on her toes
> With her baby on her knee and through the world she goes
> Up the heathery mountain and down the rushy glen
> We dare not go a-hunting for Conor and his men.

Another version of this song known as *Up The Heathery Mountains,* collected in Belfast, was used by the poet William Allingham from Ballyshannon for his poem *The Fairies.*

Up the heathery mountains and down the rushy glen
We dare not go a-hunting for Conor and his men
They are all lusty bachelors but one I knew
And that's (Tom Mulligan) the flower of the flock
He is the flower of the flock he is the keeper of the glen
He courted (Kate O'Neill) before he was a man
He huggled her, he guggled her, he took her on his knee
Saying my bonnie (Kate O'Neill) won't you marry me?

So (Kate O'Neill) made a pudding so nice and so sweet
And Tom got out his knife and cut it round and neat
Saying taste love and don't say no
For next Sunday to church we will go
With rings on our fingers and bells on our toes
And a little baby in her arms and that's the way she goes
And here's a clap, and here's a clap for Mrs ____'s daughter.

A full description of the game does not exist, although Clara M.
Patterson says that the game was very widely known and adds the
brief description: "One child is in the centre of a circle of children,
who dance round singing."

22. Round About The Ladies

Marching round the ladies, marching round the ladies
Marching round the ladies, as you have done before.

In and out the windows, in and out the windows
In and out the windows, as you have done before.

Stand and face your lover, stand and face your lover
Stand and face your lover, as you have done before.

Follow him (her) to London, follow him (her) to London
Follow him (her) to London, as you have done before.

Chase him (her) back to Belfast, chase him (her) back to Belfast
Chase him (her) back to Belfast, as you have done before.

This is a variation of a rhyme called *Round About The Village,* a ring game in which the players take hands and stand in an extended circle while a single player marches round and round the outside of the circle as they sing. At the second verse the arms are raised to form an arch between each player forming the ring, in and out of which the single player now threads his or her way, going to the centre during the third verse to stand and face the chosen "lover". As the fourth verse is sung the lover pursues the first player, who must endeavour to reach the vacant place thus left in the circle without being caught or he retires from the game. In any case his place is taken outside the circle by the chosen lover and the game is resumed. This game is similar to *Dusty Bluebells,* which eventually replaced it in popularity.

23. Here's An Oul' Widow

This is a mixed boys and girls game. All join hands to form a ring. A girl takes her stand in the centre while the rest are walking or dancing around and singing:

Oh here's an oul' widow she lies alone
She lies alone, she lies alone
Oh here's an oul' widow she lies alone
She wants a man an' she can't get none

Chose one, choose two
Choose the fairest of you

The fairest one that I can see
Is (Paddy McGuffin) come over to me.

Having been chosen Paddy leaves the ring and joins the "oul' widow". The rest then resume their dancing round and sing:

An' now she's married an' tied till a bag
An' tied till a bag, an' tied till a bag
An' now she's married an' tied till a bag
An' married a man with a wooden leg.

> Choose one, choose two
> Choose the fairest of you
>
> The fairest one that I can see
> Is (Paddy McGuffin) come over to me.

The game can then recommence as above.
The following is another Belfast variation:

> There was an old soldier he came from the wars
> His age was sixty and one
> Go you old soldier and choose a wife
> Choose a good one or choose none.
>
> Here's a poor widow she lives her lone
> She hasn't a daughter to marry but one
> Choose to the east choose to the west
> And choose to the very one you like best.
>
> Here's a couple married in joy
> First a girl and then a boy
> Seven years after and seven years to come
> Pray young people, kiss and have done.

This appears to be a combination of the "Oul' Widow" and some other game.

Another version of this song is known as *Soldier:*

> I am an old soldier, I come from the war,
> Come from the war.
> I am an old soldier, I come from the war,
> And my age it is sixty and three.
>
> I have but one son and he lies alone,
> Lies alone.
> I have but one son and he lies alone,
> And he's still making moan for lying alone.
>
> Son go choose a wife of your own,
> Choose a good one or else choose none,
> Or bring none home to me.

Now they're married, they're bound to obey,
Bound to obey in *every degree*,
And as you go round kiss all but me.

The players form a ring and sing the first three verses. Then one of the players chooses a girl from the ring. The first three verses are again sung until the whole ring is arranged in couples. Then the first couple kneel in the middle, while the rest dance around them singing the last verse after which each couple kiss. Then a second couple kneel in the middle, get married and kiss and so the game continues until all the couples are married.

THE MAIDS OF BELFAST

Here she stands a lovely creature
Who she is I cannot tell
I will court her for her beauty
For she is a handsome belle.

Children's song

Spinning and winding

Love songs always follow a predictable story line. The writer is generally out walking along by a river, grove or wood. He meets a "fair maid" who is so beautiful that she is compared to a Greek or Roman goddess. In some cases she is beyond even their beauty. The colour of her hair is commented on, her cheeks are "like roses red", and the eyes can be as "black as sloes". The suitor showers the maid with flowery compliments trying to find out where she comes from. The maid describes herself in lowly terms ("I am no equal match for you") whereupon the suitor proposes to her. On occasion she will accept ("she gave consent at last") or will refuse the offer because she is already betrothed ("the lad I admire has crossed the main"). She will then sing her true lover's praises and leave the jilted suitor in despair ("home I went with discontent"). A persistent suitor will not take no for an answer and will persevere only to get another refusal followed by more professions of love for her true love who is away at sea or war. In some cases at this point, moved by her loyalty, the suitor reveals his true identity as the returned lover. So off they go to the church to get married and live happily ever after in sweet Belfast town.

24. The Charming Belfast Lass

The area in this song, published in 1825, is Carrick Hill (now Upper Library Street) and Henry Street, which runs between North Queen Street and York Street. The firm of Thomas and Andrew Mulholland built a cotton spinning mill in Henry Street in 1822; known as the York Street Mill, it became the biggest mill in Europe and continued in business until 1951. The magnificent organ in the Ulster Hall was presented by Andrew Mulholland in 1862.

The Charming Belfast Lass

It was on a morning fair and clear,
   As walking up by Carrick Hill
The sunny beams were shining bright,
   As passing down by York Street mill.
That edifice appeared so nice,
   Where crowds of fair maids there did pass,
But one she stole my heart away,
   She was a charming Belfast Lass.

I stepped up to this fair maid
   And unto her these words did say,
Fair maid you have my heart betrayed,
   You're fairer than the Queen of May;
Will you go to yon rural plain
   Where you and I shall have a pass,
There I'll reveal my love-sick tale
   To you my charming Belfast Lass.

She gave consent away we went,
   Unto a crystal river clear,
We both sat down upon the ground
   Where no one but ourselves could hear;
It's to my breast I closely pressed
   This fair maid on the flowery grass;
No king could be more blessed than we,
   Me and my charming Belfast Lass.

Our talk of love was all sincere
    As on the flowery banks we lay,
Hoping for ever to be blest
    And to appoint a wedding day;
All anguish from us quickly fled,
    As golden hours did o'er us flee,
In hymen banns we longed to join,
    Me and my charming Belfast Lass.

Straight up to church next day we went,
    To get the nuptial marriage tie,
For ever more for to be blest;
    In peace and love and harmony,
We spent the cheerful festive night,
    While o'er a sparkling flowing glass;
Now Mary Brown of high renown,
    She is my charming Belfast Lass.

25. The Belfast Lass

A love song from a ballad sheet published by Swindell's in Manchester. This one is laced with classical references. Cupid, of course, is the Roman god of love whose "fatal dart" has amorously wounded the songwriter. Flora is the goddess of flowers and there is hardly a love song that does not make reference to her. This lady's love will not be bought by "wealth and gold"; she aspires to much higher goals.

The Belfast Lass

When I was young and in my prime, and free from care and strife,
  I made it my choice for to pursue a sweet and single life,
Until I came to fair Belfast town, where sly Cupid bound me fast,
  His fatal dart quite wounded me when I saw the Belfast lass.

The first time that I saw this maid was in the Month of June,
  When Flora spreads her flowery robes, and small birds did sweetly tune;
But she is chief of nature's art, as she gracefully did pass,
  For pleasant, gentle, kind and free is the charming Belfast lass.

Being much confused in my mind, I approached this fair maid,
  Are you the flower of this isle, I to this sweet creature said,
I have much wealth and gold in store, to you I'll bind it fast,
  If you consent to give me your hand, my charming Belfast lass.

Like the queen of love she did express, with look both chaste and mild,
  Your riches, Sir, I covet not, gold ne'er shall me beguile,
The heart that's true is what I prize, that's the treasure that doth last,
  When gold and riches might be gone, said the charming Belfast lass.

Then carelessly she passed along, her cheeks like the rosy morn;
  No man, said she, shall me delude, and then laugh me to scorn;
I am free from care and strife, though I've not got much cash,
  Yet I am happy and content, said the charming Belfast lass.

Her sentiments confounded me, I then bid her good bye,
  I soon sail'd to America my fortune for to try,
Tho' wealth and splendour there abound, fate has my lot so cast,
  There's none on earth so dear to me, as the charming Belfast lass.

Now fortune has to me prov'd kind, I'm safe return'd again,
  No more I'll roam through foreign parts, nor cross the raging main;
When she found my heart was true, she gave consent at last,
  Then with a flowing glass in hand, I'll toast the Belfast lass.

26. The Maid Of Belfast Town

Published in Belfast in 1826, this is the most interesting and the oldest song in this section. It is one of those rural love songs that could be set anywhere in Ireland; it abounds with references to Greek and Roman gods and goddesses but more important is the internal rhyme in every alternate line, a device which was common in Gaelic verse. In the late eighteenth and early nineteenth centuries Irish was a dying language but some composers were still trying to come to grips with English and were more familiar and at ease with the rhythms and cadences of their native tongue.

The song could well have been penned by an eighteenth century hedge-school master as these scholars often composed songs employing the rhyme-schemes and metres of Gaelic poetry and filled their songs with references from Latin and Greek mythology.

The Maid Of Belfast Town

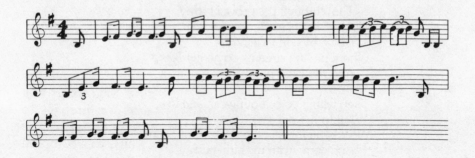

In Belfast town of high renown,
    There lives a comely maid,
Perfect complete and consummate,
    She has my heart betrayed,
She outshines by far the morning star,
    Or the moon that rules the night,
When first I saw this damsel fair,
    I was deprived of senses quite.

Diana fair cannot compare,
    Or Venus from the tide,
Or Dido sure that virgin pure,
    That for Aeneas died,
They were ne'er so fair nor could compare,
    To this damsel of renown,
Had I command of all the land,
    My love should wear the crown.

I stood amazed and on her gazed,
    In contemplating fear,
A while I roved within the grove,
    But at length to her drew near,
Are you a maid to her I said,
    That's the mistress of this grove,
Or Thesis bright that yields delight,
    That from the sea has roved.

Like an organ sweet mild and discreet,
　　She addressed herself straight away,
I ne'er did roam far from my home,
　　Tho' through the groves I stray,
My dwelling place is easy known
　　Down by yon valley wide,
Where purling streams do gently flow,
　　And run clear on every side.

Then with a voice both weak and low,
　　I unto her did say,
Would you forsake those pleasant plains,
　　And come with me straightway,
My habitation you may view
　　Down by a riverside,
Where lofty hills surround the vales and
　　Flowers on every side.

Like Aurora fair she expressed herself,
　　Or Juno from above,
Her beauty so entangled me,
　　I was scarce able to remove.
I have passed a vow I'll tell you now,
　　This seven long years before,
It's in vain for you to complain,
　　So trouble me no more.

In great disclaim she crossed the plain,
　　And left me there alone,
The small birds join a melody
　　Lamenting my sad moan,
Arise young man I pray march on,
　　Your heart is betrayed,
And do not blame this charming dame,
　　That was before engaged.

Then I fancied in my mind,
　　What those small birds said,
How they advised me to go home,
　　And leave that pleasant shade,
Then home I went with discontent,
　　My heart overflowed with care,
You powers divine with me combine,
　　And save me from despair.

So now I wander all alone,
    Down by the flowing tide,
Since that angel bright my heart's delight,
    Refused to be my bride,
Each night I dream, rave and complain,
    And can find no rest,
The pain I endure no man can cure,
    That lies within my breast.

27. The Belfast Beauty and The Kinnegar

A song composed by a local poet who lived at 97 Albert Bridge Road with the grand name of Julius Lecky McCullough Craig (1860-1935). He journeyed on foot around Ulster, Connaught and Leinster carrying sandwich boards which were adorned with his poetry and songs, ballad sheets or pictures of royalty:

My poem and picturing journey from September 1886 till 1905 through towns and townland houses of fourteen counties, a most exhaustive walk and talk... was eventful in providentially rescuing eight lives, three farmers, one labourer, one commercial traveller, one young school mistress, two young girls... I had the approval, in 18 years, of 11,268 dinners and teas.

He published a book entitled *Songs and Poems on Ireland North, South, East and West.* He often frequented Bangor to recite and sell his poems and wrote:

Why do you stay in the town all day
Amidst the strife and clangour
When you might skim in your boat so trim
From Belfast down to Bangor.

The poem with which he was most popularly associated was *The Kinnegar.*

The Kinnegar

On Carrick shore I stood and stood, and gazed across at Hollywood,
And thonder in the distance far, I saw my love a-wavin' from the Kinnegar.

The brakers riz as high as high, the screachin' wind got worse forbye,
But thonder was my golden star, a-wavin' from the Kinnegar.

I got out me boat an' rowed an' rowed, across Knockfergus bay she go'ed,
No wind or wave could hold me far, for thonder was my golden star.

Now the years have cum an' gone an' went, now I'm oul' and grey an' bent,
I'm married to a woman now, her that waved me from the Kinnegar.

Now whiles I sit an' stare an' stare an' think on that day in Carrick there,
An' wish to God I'd been drowned afar, afore I reached the Kinnegar.

The Belfast Beauty

You lads and gay lasses that rove through Parnassus
I pray pay attention to a poor wounded blade
I think it my duty to extol the beauty
Of a charming fair maiden that has me betrayed
In Donegall Street whom I chanced to meet
This beautiful damsel who does me annoy
I thought she was Flora or lovely Aurora
Or Helen the cause of the downfall of Troy.

I being much amazed right earnest I gazed
On this blooming fair one I vow and protest
This beautiful girl her teeth like the pearl
The lilies outvied by her snowy white breast
Her eyes like two diamonds delightfully shining
Her cheeks like the roses her hair a light brown
She's the fairest the rarest to me she's the dearest
Of all other maidens in sweet Belfast town.

I then stepped up to her more sharply to view her
She appeared like an angel that came from above
In this land of Erin you'll ne'er find her equal
Her aspect as meek and as mild as a dove
If Clio fair or Queen Dido was there
Neither Juno nor Venus of fame and renown
I vow and declare they could never compare
To the angelic beauty of sweet Belfast town.

Not one muse of the nine but my love can outshine
She excites the flow of the soul full in me
In this town of great fame she upholds a good name
Her greatness and goodness are known o'er the sea
Then think not I'll wed or by another be once led
For her powers of love so much virtue does prove
She has won me completely from all other maids round
Thus I title her the beauty of sweet Belfast town.

Had I wealth and grandeur like Great Alexander
That noble commander who lived in days of yore
All earthly treasure I'd resign then with pleasure
To wed with this damsel whom I do adore
Or was I the monarch of a European nation
There is none but my darling should possess the crown
The hands of dame nature ne'er formed a creature
To equal the beauty of sweet Belfast town.

One half of a town in the province of Leinster
The first twice in station with one fourth of a fowl
And when it's completely placed in arrangement
The next in rotation it must be a vowel
The name of a berry that is much admired
Neither add nor subtract but when it's penned down
It will spell you the name of this charming fair dame
That I title the beauty of sweet Belfast Town.

28. Belfast Town

Belfast Town is a very old ballad, from which Professor Robert Hanna borrowed in writing his version of *The Cavehill Diamond* (number 4 in this collection).

Belfast Town

Belfast Town, now rich and great,
    Was then a village small,
And flocks of sheep grazed on that spot,
    Where stands the Linen Hall.

To herd the sheep was Mary's task,
    And she did not repine;
She looked so happy in her flock,
    She seemed almost divine.

And at that time young Dermott lived;
    The royal crown he wore;
He ruled the ground from Belfast town
    To Mourne's mountain shore.

To hunt the bear and savage wolf
    Was this young Prince's pride;
One day of age he killed three
    Beneath the Cave Hill side.

Returning from his weary chase,
    To give his horse some rest;
The reins upon his neck lay loose,
    To give his horse some breath.

And as he rode he Mary spied,
    Who rose in deep alarm;
She was sleeping on a primrose bank,
    With her cheek upon her arm.

And as she rose the Prince she knew,
    And quickly genuflexed;
She knew him by the golden star
    That glittered on his breast.

"O! maiden tell me who art thou,
    That dazzle so my eyes?
Are you a goddess from the skies,
    Or princess in disguise?"

"Oh, banter not a maiden fair,
    Of a low and mean degree,
My sovereign prince your pardon crave;"
    With that she bent her knee.

"For I am of a lowly birth,
    And poverty beside,
My widowed mother lives with me,
    Upon the Lagan side."

"Say that you are poor no more;
    Since those sweet charms of yours
Are far beyond in priceless wealth
    All gold or silver store.

"Come with me and be my bride;
    Here is my heart and hand;
And I will share my throne with you
    As Queen of Erin's land."

Once more her snow white hand he pressed
    As they walked side by side,
Until they to the cottage came,
    Where her mother did reside.

"My worthy dame," out spoke the Prince
    (The Prince of Mourne's land),
"The man has blessing on his youth
    That has thy daughter's hand."

"My worthy prince," replied the dame,
   "It's seventeen years and more
Since her I found outside my door,
   Half buried in the snow.

"And around her neck were jewels fine,
   And likewise gold in store,
To meet all charges till the time
   I might the child restore."

And when the Prince the necklace saw,
   He started with delight,
Saying: "Mary, dear, great is thy birth,
   And great's thy wealth and right.

"You are my uncle's long lost child,
   Which shall not be denied,
Since I have found at once this day
   A cousin and a bride."

And when this royal pair was wed
   There rose with one loud roar
A general cheer from Belfast Lough
   To Mourne's mountain shore.

THE RAKES OF BELFAST

The lasses all where'er I steer,
They say I am a raker.

Roving Jack The Baker

Botanical Gardens

During the early nineteenth century Belfast could be an unruly place at night with drunkards, ruffians and prostitutes roaming the streets. As far back as 1792 there were one hundred and nineteen publicans in Belfast, or one pub to every sixteen houses. Public figures did not exactly set an example in the consumption of alcohol for at public dinners as many as twenty-four, thirty-two, forty-one or even forty-four toasts might be drunk (*News Letter* 1802, 1804, 1819, 1822). By 1819 there were at least eighty-eight public houses and taverns in the town, many of which were situated in North Street, Ann Street and the entries off High Street. There was certainly plenty of work for the Ulster Temperance Society when it eventually started its campaign against alcohol in 1829.

In 1811 it was reported that "a daring banditti of nocturnal robbers have infested the streets for some nights past…" and that the town had "neither guard, guard house or gaol". It was not until 1816 that a regular and permanent night watch was established in the town. Written reports were kept by the officers who frequently referred to the women who "infested" the streets in large numbers as "ill-behaved, whores, idle women, nymphs, riotous females and abandoned women". In October of that year during rioting in the streets many people were set upon and savagely beaten. It was said that the town was "a sink of iniquity for no-one can walk the street after night in safety". Even by 1824 many of these problems remained and Cornmarket was described as "a den of blackguards and an eternal bear garden where pugilistic drunkards and pickpockets reign undisputed".

Such then is the setting for some of these songs all of which embody the same themes of carousing and womanising.

29. The Belfast Cockabendy

A colourful account of the amorous pursuits of one Cockabendy.
There was in fact such a person with that nickname in Belfast: he
was a fiddle player and a very shrewd one at that because no matter
what locality he played in he always had an appropriate tune to suit
the persuasion of the inhabitants. *Garryowen, Patrick's Day* and
The Boyne Water were the favourites. At seventy-five years of age
he had his bed, blankets and spinning-wheel seized by his landlord to
whom he owed ten shillings. After that Cockabendy fell on such hard
times that the *News Letter* made an appeal on his behalf. The newspaper referred to him as "the harmless and entertaining character".
It was stated that any contributions received would be "repaid
thankfully by that eminent violin performer". Appropriately enough,
the song, which was printed in Belfast in 1817, concludes with a
fine quatrain in praise of the city.

The Belfast Cockabendy

You lads and lasses brisk and gay
I pray you pay attention
And listen now to what I'll say
Perhaps some things I'll mention
Which may your jealousy provoke
Or else 'twill please your fancy
We will pass it over as a joke
And I will kiss my Nancy.

When you come to Belfast town
Come not without some shillings
And you had better bring a pound
To make the lasses willing
Then if you wish a bit of fish
Go take a drop of brandy
And if you choose they'll not refuse
To play up cockabendy.

As I was walking up North Street
I being in good apparel
I on the way did chance to meet
A smiling pretty girl
Straight to a dram shop then we went
To take a drop of brandy
And home we went with one consent
To play up cockabendy.

Then with my smiling little friend
We being but one couple
A crown or two I had to spend
Because I spoiled her ruffle
My watch my chain and golden seal
While I was full of brandy
Out of my fob they were conveyed
While playing cockabendy.

Then up to Carrick Hill I strayed
In serious contemplation
Bestowing on the smiling maid
Many an execration
A light I spied and in I hied
Where they were drinking brandy
And a bonny lass reached me a glass
And welcomed cockabendy.

I then lay down to take a sleep
And swore away all sorrow
Determining from home to keep
Until the other morrow
When I awoke my hat and coat
I found were pledged for brandy
And I got fire without a smoke
While playing cockabendy.

The two last crowns which I had found
Went to release my garments
They searched my fob for other Joes
Which caused me much alarm
The wicked Queen did curse and swear
That she should have more brandy
And I paid the piper let who will dance
To the tune of cockabendy.

When over the long bridge I strayed
As I thought free from danger
I turned in to see a maid
To whom I was no stranger
Said if you run your pretty face
Trust for one pint of brandy
I'll surely pay next market day
And we'll play cockabendy.

It's I presume you're short of cash
The damsel she retorted
And you have lost your silver watch
Wherever you resorted
Begone you dirty drunken sot
Where e'er you drank your brandy
Then right across the nose she struck
Poor simple cockabendy.

The Belfast lads they say are prone
For to love the lasses
The lasses I am sure are prone
For to love their glasses
Botany Bay's the place they take their tea
Carrick Hill their brandy
And Mill Street is a bonny place
For playing cockabendy.

30. The Young Man Badly Walked

A song set in High Street and York Street in the late 1870s. The Albert Clock was completed in 1869 and chignons or buns and the bustle or Grecian Bend were the fashion of the time. The reference to the "long bridge" is misleading since this was probably the Queen's Bridge and not the Long Bridge, which had twenty arches, was 2,562 feet long and was demolished in 1842 to make way for the Queen's Bridge. William's Lane ran off Great Patrick Street, which was a continuation of Fredrick Street.

The Young Man Badly Walked

I am a jolly roving blade and do belong to Donaghadee,
I like to sup to cheer me up. I'm always jolly kind and free,
I dress myself all in my best, new, and shirt as white as chalk,
With watch and chain, and lots of cash I was not badly walked.

I took the train to famed Belfast the day being wet I entered in,
To a public house was near and there my spree I did begin,
I filled my pipe and called my glass the whiskey was the best of malt,
When up it cleared and out I steered and over the long bridge walked.

At night I strolled down High Street, to view the nights and beauties there,
By chance I met a little pet she was possessed of beauty rare,
Her bewitching eye as she passed by struck me like an electric shock,
If that lass speaks and I as a treat says I, I won't be badly walked.

With courage bold then I stepped up and did salute this little dear,
Saying if you have time will you incline to a drop of whiskey rum or beer,
She smiled and said excuse me sir, I am on an errand and can't stop,
But she did consent and in we went I thought I was not badly walked.

Into a public house we went I called for brandy punch made hot,
Glass after glass around did pass till the Albert Clock struck ten o'clock,
Then to amaze those words she says, kind sir I can no longer stop,
But you can come and see me home, all right my dear, so out we walked.

All was not right quite the reverse she said she came to meet a friend,
She wore a chignon stylish hat a tunic and skirt and Grecian Bend,
She looked so neat and smiled so sweet concerning love was our talk,
I felt much cheered with my dear to William's Lane we walked.

She introduced me to a friend and said it was her cousin Kate,
Saying can this young man stop here, the night's advancing late,
He was so kind I'll speak my mind he's the first man has stole my heart.
If he constant proves he will share my love and from him never part.

All right again my pretty dame tomorrow we'll get wed,
The landlady says if you're going to stay pay 5s for your bed,
I paid the cash I had a glass I smoked my pipe and talked,
She smiled and says, love come away, and up stairs we were walked.

In the morning I awoke, and found myself alone,
My watch and chain, ten pounds in cash, my coat and boots were gone,
I rapped and said where is the maid that brought me here to stop,
When a chap let fly and bunged my eye get out you're badly walked.

By the hair dragged me down stair and out he threw me on the street,
Like a dying codfish there I lay I was foundered complete,
I strove to run it was no fun my feet against the stones I knocked,
The women's cry as I passed by, my lad you're badly walked.

Now all you simple country lads if e'er you go out on a spree,
Some ladies fair would you ensnare bear in mind how they served me,
I tell you true you will surely rue no matter what they say or talk,
If you go to William's Lane you'll find you will be badly walked.

31. The Sailor's Hornpipe In Caxon Street

This song is currently enjoying a new lease of life under various titles such as *Barrack Street, Sackville Street, The Shifting Apron* and *The Sporting Sailor Boy*. Caxon Street or Caxton Street was off Lower Donegall Street and ran parallel to Academy Street. Jackson Street ran from North Boundary Street to Hudson Street off the Lower Falls Road.

It was originally published by Nicholson's of Church Lane, Belfast.

The Sailor's Hornpipe In Caxon Street

Good people pay attention, and listen to my song,
I'll sing to you a verse or two, I won't detain you long;
I came home from sea the other day, a fair lass I did meet,
She asked me to go along with her, and dance in Jackson's Street.

"Jack, as you can't dance too well, will you then have a treat?
Will you have a glass of brandy, or something you may take?
At nine o'clock this evening I'll see you at the train;
And if ever you come this road, Jack, you will give us a call again."

When the dinner was over, the whiskey did come in;
Then round the floor with Maggie I danced the merry tune,
And the other couple they did dance
A double-shuffle all round the room.

When the supper was over I prepared and went to bed,
I shortly fell asleep, the truth, I do declare;
When I awakened in the morning nothing could I spy,
But a woman's shift and apron that at the foot of the bed did lie.

The daylight was past, and the night was coming on,
I put on the shift and apron – to the quay I did run;
And when I got my foot aboard, the sailors they did say,
"By my word, Jack, you have caught the clock since you've been away!"

"Is that the new Spring fashion they've got upon the shore?
Where is the shop they sell them – do you think there are any more?"
Says the Captain to me, "Jack I thought you were for Newry bound?
You might have got a better suit than that for less than three pounds."

"I met a girl in Heyberry Street; she asked me away to dance,
She stole away my heart with her roguish Irish glance;
She danced to my destruction – I suffered so complete,
I'll take my oath I'll go no more to dance in Jackson Street."

Come all you jolly seamen, a warning take by me,
Be sure to choose a comrade before you get on the spree,
Be sure and keep out of Jackson Street, or you will rue the day
With a woman's shift and apron you will have to go to sea.

32. Roving Jack The Baker

The tune of this song is very well known in its own right as *Merrily Kiss The Quaker,* although the tune has three parts.

Caddell's Entry was so called after Edward Caddell, an attorney who came to Belfast from Rathfriland. The following advertisement appeared in a local newspaper on 13 April 1756:

To be let by Edward Caddell for 21 or 31 years from first day of May next, four new houses almost completely finished in the entry facing the Market House of Belfast. N.B. He intends to make a new street or widen the entry from High Street to Rosemary Lane and that for the future no stables shall be kept therein.

Caddell's Entry and Legg's Lane were demolished in 1865 and Legg's Lane is now the site of the west side and Caddell's Entry the east side of Lombard Street, which was opened in 1874.

Roving Jack The Baker

Come all you jolly roving blades,
   I pray you give attention,
I've just returned from the wars,
   And got a right good pension,
The lasses all where'er I steer,
   They say I am a raker,
I treat them to good punch and beer,
   I'm roving Jack the baker.

It was in Belfast I met a lass,
   To treat her was right willing,
So we went in to take a glass,
   With her I spent a shilling,
I spoke so plain to this young dame,
   She took me for a Quaker,
I let her know before she did go,
   I was roving Jack the baker.

Fifteen pound she had in gold,
   Which caus'd me to be funny,
A thousand lies to her I told,
   All for to get her money,
I courted her with such an air,
   She asked me if I'd take her,
It was good news, I do declare,
   For roving Jack the baker.

My dear, I said, and charming maid,
   You are my joy and treasure,
My tender heart you have ensnared,
   I love you beyond measure,
I did declare solemnly aware,
   That night a bride I'd make her,
Although I promised her so fair,
   No mind had Jack the baker.

Then how to act I could not tell,
   All methods there I tried,
Her money I did like right well,
   But not her for my bride,
Then to be married we did go,
   But absent was our speaker,
Which fill'd my darling's heart with woe,
   Rejoiced was Jack the baker.

Said I, my dear, you need not fear,
   Surely a bride I'll make you,
While blood remains within my veins,
   I never will forsake you,
To Caddell's Entry, straight we went,
   A lodging there did take her,
To have her gold was my intent,
   Fine fun for Jack the baker.

My charmer and I went into bed,
   I folded her in my arms,
No matter what I did or said,
   I rifled all her charms,
The liquor there I did not spare,
   Quite tipsy I did make her,
If she had died I did not care,
   Content was Jack the baker.

At last my charmer fell asleep,
   Time for me to be going,
I out of bed did gently creep,
   'Twas almost cock crowing,
The door after me I did not shut,
   For fear I should awake her,
Her gold into my pocket put,
   Farewell to Jack the baker.

33. The Connaught Man's Trip To Belfast

Carrick Hill End was in the Upper Library Street area. The steam train to Lisburn had been in operation since August 1839. Caxton Street was off Lower Donegall Street and ran parallel to Academy Street. Not too far away was Walker's Lane, which ran off Fredrick Street.

Picking oakum was the teasing out and untwisting of old ropes used for stopping up or caulking the seams of ships.

The Connaught Man's Trip To Belfast

I am a poor Connaught man from the town of Athlone,
    And I wish from my heart I had never left home,
I came to Belfast to look out for a friend,
    And I met a young lady near Carrick Hill End.
        With my fal da la la.

She says now kind sir you are going astray,
    But if you come with me I will show you the way,
She hoisted me to Lisburn and carried my coat,
    Like thunder we galloped behind the steam coach.

She went into an inn and she called for some wine,
    She told the inn-keeper she was a cousin of mine,
She called a hot dinner and punch there galore,
    When she says, "cousin Pat it is time to go home."

Then we both to the steam coach without more delay,
    And straight into Belfast we cantered away,
She called for a car so as to not wet my feet,
    She brought me and my coat into sweet Caxton Street.

Every blackguard came in he shook hands with poor Pat,
    They had all kinds of liquor and kept me in chat,
At the hour of twelve my land-lady came down,
    Says she for the reckoning just pay me one pound.

I paid her the money without more delay,
    And to Walker's Lane I cantered away,
She called for a bed and lay down by my side,
    So the poor Connaught man had a beautiful bride.

But they blackened my face when they got me asleep,
    At the dead of the night they threw me out on the street,
I called "whill aloe" for my money and clothes,
    Then the police came up saying you're drunk I suppose.

To the new police office they took me away,
    Locked me in a cell for a night and a day,
And sent me to prison where I made sad moans,
    Where they made me pick oakum and also break stones.

I had forty-five pounds that I stole from my aunt,
    I'll make you all laugh at my unlucky jaunt,
Not a fiddler or piper ever played in a fair,
    Could play the same tunes that they make you dance there.

When I got out of gaol I made home once more,
    The hair of my head and my whiskers were shorn,
And supping their porridge I scalded my nose,
    So the poor Connaught man lost his money and clothes.

THE PORT OF BELFAST

To Belfast town we all went down our passage for to take.

The Loss Of The Lady Of The Lake

Steam and sail in Spenser Basin

Lloyd's List records that between 1846 and 1850 there were 12,263 sailing vessels lost or involved in other disasters. 9,268 were driven ashore, wrecked, foundered, abandoned or lost without trace, while 2,665 managed to struggle into port after sustaining heavy damage. Every year sixty ships sailed into oblivion never to be seen again. Around the United Kingdom coasts alone during the same period of 1846 to 1850 there were 3,100 casualties per year. Despite the dangers of the sea, trade with Belfast in the early 1880s showed no signs of abating. It was well established as a port for both passenger and goods vessels. The "Belfast Ship News" column in the *News Letter* gave details of the constant arrivals and departures and numerous private shipping companies competed for business with advertisements in local newspapers. There were sailings to London, Bristol, Liverpool, Glasgow and even to such far-flung places as Barbados, Baltimore, New York and Quebec.

The "Ship News" generally ended with wind reports which were of great significance to ship owners since sailings were totally at the mercy of wind, wave and tide. Steam ships did not come into use until later in the century. Storms constantly created havoc for ship-owners and each storm brought a litany of casualties in its wake. Shipwreck reports, such as this from 28 May 1822, eventually filtered back to the "Ship News" column:

The Schooner Lark Hill from Jamaica for Belfast... on 11th ult. during a gale, upset; the master and crew drowned – only one passenger saved, who was taken off the wreck...

That anybody ever survived being shipwrecked seems extraordinary but many did and lived to tell the story or sing the song. The "Ship News" frequently carried horrific accounts of shipwrecks as described by survivors. This constant danger of being shipwrecked was, of course, in addition to the many other hazards posed by physical conditions on board ship. Cramped conditions, near starvation and frequent outbreaks of disease or "ship fever" had also to be contended with. The fact that so many emigrants risked their lives on the sea speaks for their desperation to escape more pressing hardships at home and their determination to make a new start.

34. Lovely Ann or The Loss Of The Ship Union

An advertisement appeared in the *News Letter* of 19 March 1822:
For St. Andrews, New Brunswick, The Brig Union of Workington.
Matthew Armstrong Master.

This vessel is expected to arrive here about the latter end of this month. She is well known in the Passenger Trade as a comfortable conveyance and will sail for the above Port three weeks after arrival. For Freight and Passage apply to
T.G. FOLINGSBY
7, Hanover Quay.

On 9 April another advertisement appeared:
The Union is Single Birthed and Capt. Armstrong being Owner of this Vessel, will as usual, pay every attention during the voyage to the comfort of Passengers.

For Freight or Passenger please apply to the Captain on Board, at the Long Bridge…

On 7 May passengers were requested "to be in Belfast on Friday 10th May to pay remainder of Passage Money and go on board as the Vessel will be dispatched without delay after that date." The "Ship News" of 14 May announced that: "the Brig Union, Armstrong, for St. Andrews… clear tomorrow and sails first fair wind."

But on 28 May the *News Letter* carried the following report:
The Brig Union, of Workington, [under] Captain Armstrong, sailed from Belfast on the 16th. inst. with about 120 passengers on board for St. Andrews, New Brunswick, and on the evening of the same day, about ten o'clock the vessel, in a thick fog, with a strong current struck upon the rocks on the South East side of Rathlin Island at a place called Achill Bay and soon filled with water, threatening a watery grave to all on board. This would have been their inevitable lot had the vessel struck on the rock two lengths of herself lower down, but by the praiseworthy exertions of the master and mate all the crew and passengers were saved and got ashore on the rocks together with the principal part of their provisions. The news of their distress soon spread on the Island and they found consolation and relief in the kind attention

of the Rev. R. Gape resident about two miles from the wreck, who at once showed himself the father and friend of the distressed and with Lieu. Murray of the water-guard, not only protected their property, but sheltered the persons of many of the passengers. And here it is due to the Island to state, that it is not only free from those bands of plunderers which infest other coasts but that a kindred feeling seems to prevail among the islanders in taking a share in the misfortunes of the distressed. The agent of this vessel, with a promptness almost unequalled, appeared on the Island early on Sunday and cheered the passengers by a promise that they should not only be sent back to Belfast, but that their passage money should be all refunded. This has since been done – an instance of liberality rarely equalled. We regret to hear that the vessel had only been insured to the amount of 200 guineas, one sixteenth share.

Many of the details in the song contradict those reported in the *News Letter.* The song gives a different date for the sailing and says that it took the ship three days to get to Rathlin Island; also, the sea is described as "mountains high" when, in fact, the ship foundered due to thick fog. There is no mention of the help given to the stricken sailors by the people of Rathlin. In spite of all the apparent inaccuracies the song was published on ballad sheets and chapbooks for many years after the event.

Lovely Ann
or
The Loss Of The Ship Union

When I was young and in my prime
The seas I had to rove
My friends together did combine
To part me from my love
To Belfast town they me conveyed
Without any more delay
And in the Union my passage paid
Bound for America.

It was on the fourteenth day of May
From Belfast we set sail
It was down the lough we bore away
With a sweet and pleasant gale
Farewell to the Shamrock Shore
And bonny banks of Bann
And the sweet girl I adore
My charming lovely Ann.

For Saint Andrews we were bound
Our course for to steer
From Erin's shore away we bore
Thinking no danger near
At ten o'clock on the third night
We got a dreadful shock
Our ship dashed with all her might
Against a dreadful rock.

Then our hard fate for to lament
It's now we do begin
In discontent some hours we spent
Then south east of Rathlin
Overboard our stores we threw
With all our cargo brave
Numbers to the shrouds then flew
Their precious lives to save.

The raging seas ran mountains high
And dismal were the skies
No light or land could we espy
And horrid were the cries
It was here we lay till break of day
Describe our state who can
Then to myself these words did say
Adieu sweet lovely Ann.

Soon as we got a glimpse of light
Our boats we did employ
Towards the shore we took our flight
Our hearts did leap with joy
Providence to us was kind
His name we do adore
There's not a soul was left behind
We all got safe to shore.

Now farewell to America
And the rocks of Rathlin
No more I'll from my country roam
To cross the raging main
I'll go and see my bonnie lass
Down by the river Bann
And all my days with her I'll pass
My charming lovely Ann.

35. The Loss Of The Lady Of The Lake

The Belfast *News Letter* reported on 21 June 1833:

The following is a copy of a letter received by Mr. Grainger on Tuesday from Mr. Wright, one of the passengers saved from the ill-fated Lady of the Lake from this port to Quebec. It is so far satisfactory, that it affords the assurance that at least 34 passengers were rescued from death, the relations of whom will be gratified to find their names communicated in the letter:

St. John's, Newfoundland, 26th. May.

Dear Sir,

Before this can reach you, I conclude you must have heard of the most melancholy loss of the Lady of the Lake. At present I have not time to give you any of the particulars. I think it, however, my duty to the family of poor Mr. Park to inform you of his fate. The time was so short from taking the ice till the vessel went down (I feel certain not longer than 25 minutes) before she went over. I got into the stern boat (through the merest chance). I called to Park to follow me (he was standing by the chains) when he asked me if I had with me any money, in case we should reach the shore; I replied I had not thought of it; He said he would go back for his coat and if I would tell him where to find the money, he would bring it; I said he would find some sovereigns in my gun cases and also told him where to get the keys. Neither he nor I expecting the ship so soon to go down, he went back, but before he returned (and I believe he was detained in the cabin owing to the water coming in it), the vessel sunk so fast that the sailors let go the ropes and pushed out the boat. When last I saw him, I stood up and shouted to him to throw himself in the water and I would save him, for the sailors would not again approach the vessel, crowds being ready to drop into the boat; I then lost sight of him among the rush, when the Lady of the Lake fell over. I understand he tried to get into the long boat after Capt. Grant and perished in the attempt. Had he poor fellow thrown himself into the sea he would probably have been saved; Yet his friends have one consolation left, that he was fully prepared to die, as I have never met with a more religious or better disposed person from my own short acquaintance of him, I feel his loss most keenly.

My own life has been saved through the merest chance. I was out three days and three nights with eight sailors in the little stern boat without almost any protection from the weather and our escape has been a most truly miraculous one. I am now suffering much from the cold. I subjoin a list of those saved.

H. S. Wright.

The list (see Notes) mentions one passenger who was saved by a ship called the *Lima;* his name was George Monaghan and he survived to compose this song.

The *News Letter* also reported:

A letter from the mate of the Lady of the Lake has been received at Aberdeen, which states that he with eight of the crew were in the stern boat three nights and four days, when they were picked up by the Messenger of Torquay and carried into St. John's Newfoundland. Captain Grant with eleven men and two women were picked up by the Gipsy of Hamburgh and arrived at St. John's Newfoundland on 20th. May.

The Loss Of The Lady Of The Lake

Which sailed from Belfast for America
and was lost on the Banks of Newfoundland.

You inhabitants of Ireland attend to what I say,
While I relate our doleful fate going to America.
Lonesome was our funeral and dismal was our wake,
Since we have lost our passengers in the Lady of the Lake.

It was in the present year eighteen hundred and thirty-three,
We bid farewell to Ireland which proved our destiny.
Our ship was split asunder as you may understand,
Which left our bodies floating on the Banks of Newfoundland.

All you who live in Ireland and are inclined to roam,
Beware of our unhappy fate when in your native home.
To Belfast town we all went down our passage for to take,
To our grief we sailed away in the Lady of the Lake.

We had a pleasant sea my boys, three weeks and something more.
We thought good news to send again unto the Shamrock shore.
The ice came down like mountains high, which caused our hearts to ache,
And in the deep we had to lie with the Lady of the Lake.

Darkness overclouded us and dismal was the sea.
For fourteen hours in great darkness and agony we lay.
When we thought on those we left behind we thought our hearts would
    break,
To see grim death before us in the Lady of the Lake.

In the county Cavan, Monaghan and Tyrone,
We left our friends behind us, our fate to bemoan.
There was nothing there to save our lives, alas it was too late,
But now their grave lies in the deep with the Lady of the Lake.

When we found we were going down, we knew not what to do.
I swam unto a flake of ice and bid the ship adieu.
Our passengers for mercy cried, which grieved our hearts full sore.
Unto the bottom they went down and we never saw them more.

Our Captain with some sailors bold in the long boat got away.
All night upon the flake of ice in great darkness I lay,
Until the Captain of the Lima, the truth I will unfold,
Upon the 25th of May brought me for Liverpool.

Now to conclude and make an end to God I'll always pray.
'Twas he alone that saved my life from dangers of the sea.
My name it is George Monaghan I'm in existence still.
I'll live and die among my friends near the town of sweet Cootehill.

36. The Ports Are Open

This song was written in 1815 after the defeat of Napoleon Bonaparte at the battle of Waterloo. During the war between England and France the Government imposed severe restrictions on the import of cereals into British ports – "It shut up our ports against peas, beans and oats". The price of corn was high and continued to rise throughout the war. Farmers invested capital in developing inferior land and generally increasing the area of cultivation for cereal growing; yields increased and profits rose accordingly, but the ending of the war was to change all that. British ports were once more opened to the import of foreign grain and the effect on home prices was dramatic. Wheat cost 126s 6d per quarter in 1812, but in 1815 the price plummeted to 65s 7d per quarter.

The song celebrates the opening of the ports. Farmers, of course, were angry at the Government's change of policy, since many were faced with heavy losses and bankruptcy. For ordinary people, however, it was a very optimistic period with the prospect of fuller employment – "no more idle hands to be seen"; cheaper bread – "I'll wager a crown that the meal will come down"; and above all plentiful supplies – "up the Lagan tide you'll see vessels ride Well loaded with all sorts of grain, boys."

The Ports Are Open was sung to the tune of *The World It May Wag*.

The Ports Are Open

You tradesmen so brave your attention I crave
And distressed poor of this nation
You'll rejoice now to hear the glad tidings I bear
In this time of sad desolation
A great proclamation's now sent thro' each nation
For all British ports to open
To admit foreign grain to our markets again
Now the meal mongers hearts are broken.

Chorus
And farmers quite distracted they'll go
This news to them must be provoking
Provisions will flow now in spite of them all
Huzza-now the ports are all open.

These eight months and more now the labouring poor
They had not the least of enjoyment
Distressed tradesmen got the work before them
And threw most of them out of employment
But the time is drawing nigh when the shuttle will fly
And no more idle hands to be seen
May they never again have cause to complain
As the last time they met in the Strand.

Chorus

It was not only here that the times were severe
But in Britain as well as Hibernia
In Manchester they say vast numbers each day
By the hunger fever were smitten
It was here and there they had tents to prepare
For those poor starving creatures to die in
There was plenty of meat but none could they get
For want of money to buy them.

Chorus

In Belfast most brave the tradesmen did behave
And kept themselves free of all riot
While in other towns they were wrecking steam looms
But what did poor creatures make by it
There were forty-seven people sent to prison
And sentence of death they received
Their families at home they were left it's well known
Of the comfort of life quite bereaved.

Chorus

Now trade it once more will revive on our shore
Free commerce we'll have with each nation
We'll never again have cause to complain
When once freed from emancipation
Now this Corporation Bill it some hundreds did kill
While others it kept in high station
It shut up our ports against peas beans and oats
And it ruined the trade of our nation.

Chorus

I'll wager a crown that the meal will come down
The butter the beef and the tatoes
Now farmers at home may store up their grain
They'll get leave no longer to cheat us
Up the Lagan tide you'll see the vessels ride
Well loaded with all sorts of grain boys
Gold and silver once more will adorn our shore
And trade it will flourish again boys.

Chorus

Our sovereign the king now it's long may he reign
To govern the brave British realm
His subjects again won't have cause to complain
I hope while he sits at the helm
By his great command the ports open will stand
Till the twenty-fourth of December
So parliament then when they do meet again
Hope that too the poor will remember.

Chorus

37. The Brave Queen's Island Boys

In the 1830s trade with Belfast was increasing at such a rate that the port could scarcely cope. To rectify this situation extensive improvements were carried out during the 1840s along the banks of the River Lagan to the north of the Queen's Bridge. Victoria Channel was opened in 1849 and the excavated material amassed from its formation was banked up on the eastern side of the river. This reclaimed plot was called Dargan's Island after the contractor but subsequently changed to Queen's Island after Queen Victoria's visit to the town in 1849. Out of such innocuous beginnings grew a shipbuilding industry that was to gain worldwide recognition.

This reputation was largely due to the efforts of the Harland and Wolff company which was formed in 1861. Even in its infancy the company gained respect for its innovative approach to shipbuilding engineering. In 1867 it launched the *Istrian, Iberion* and *Illyrian* ships for the Bibby Line. These ships were unusual for their great length, narrow beam and "Belfast bottom" and were nicknamed "Bibby Coffins" by cynics. However, with their unrivalled speed and capacity they were soon referred to as "ocean greyhounds".

In 1870 Harland and Wolff signed a contract to build ships for the Oceanic Steam Navigation Company, better known as the White Star Line. The first ship built was the *Oceanic,* the first modern liner of its kind. The *Britannic* and the *Germanic* were launched in 1874 and were known as "flyers", cutting the Atlantic crossing time by one day to seven-and-a-half days.

The song dates from the 1880s.

The Brave Queen's Island Boys

Oh, Belfast may boast and justly of the progress it has made,
  And point with pride and pleasure to its vast and varied trade,
But none of its proud possessions either equals or outstrips,
  The gallant bands whose cunning hands,
Construct its far-famed ships.

Chorus
Then here's to the brave Queen's Island Boys,
  May their fame and fortune grow,
And their gallant ships all others eclipse,
  Where'er o'er the world they go.
May the name of Harland and Wolff still stand,
  At the top of the ship-building trade,
And their efforts ne'er cease to maintain and increase,
  The glorious repute they have made.

Oh, the Island Boys are marvels – so stalwart, strong and true,
  With no rivals throughout the Empire when there's difficult work to do,
You'll find with them no "scamping" no "shirking" or backing out,
  For whate'er they essay, whether work or play,
They go at with a will firm and stout.

Chorus

With their "White Star Liner" they shortened the way o'er the "herring
    pond's" stormy wave,
  Till the builders of Tyne, Thames and Clyde were ready almost to rave,
So whenever a "Greyhound's" needed whose work can't be surpassed,
  From the world's end they now at once send
Their contracts to be filled at Belfast.

Chorus

As citizens too the Island Boys have ever done their parts,
  When the country or their city sought the aid of hands or hearts,
Like the sturdy old Ship Carpenters, they've always plainly shown,
  Through weal or woe, with friend or foe,
That they'd stand by Church and Throne.

Chorus

38. The Shipwreck On The Lagan Canal

There are various canal songs in existence with titles such as *On Board The Bugaboo, The Thirteenth Lock, The Wreck Of The Vartry, The Wreck Of The Mary Jane,* and *The Cruise Of The Calibar.* A common theme to them all is a canal journey that ends in disaster. The tales of these calamitous expeditions are recounted with a great sense of humour. *The Shipwreck On The Lagan Canal* is no exception, being very similar in content to *The Cruise Of The Calibar.* It describes a trip from the Queen's Bridge up the Lagan Canal en route to "foreign countries" – probably Portadown!

The Shipwreck On The Lagan Canal

On the 18th of October,
   Being the day that we set sail
From the Queen's Bridge
   With a Cargo of Indian meal;
Our course being up the Lagan,
   And our Captain's name McFall
We were bound for foreign countries
   Up the Lagan Canal.

We had not long been started
   When it blew a dreadful gale,
Our Captain he gave orders
   For the Crew to shorten sail,
The sea being rolling mountains high,
   The night being very dark,
We thought that we should get ashore
   About the Ormeau Park.

For hours we were tossed about,
   And then a dreadful thump;
She struck up a coral reef –
   We all took to the pump;
We pumped away for hours;
   We were nearly dead from cold
The water gained upon us
   Being ten foot in the hold.

When we could pump no longer,
   We gave up in despair,
And soon a signal of distress
   Was flying in the air.
Our captain pulled his trumpet out,
   And loudly he did bawl,
So down she went stern foremost
   In the Lagan Canal.

The water it being very deep –
   It took us to the shin;
We had a poor chance of our lives,
   As none of us could swim.
We thought of our wives and children
   Whom we might see no more,
When a coastguard threw his muffler,
   And pulled us safe to shore.

He brought us to the Police Office,
   And he got us all a bed;
There was not one amongst us
   Hadn't the staggers in his head.
So now my song is ended,
   It's enough to please you all,
By singing you the shipwreck
   In the Lagan Canal.

POLITICS IN BELFAST

Rejoice sons of Erin all over the land,
Our noble procession was pleasant and grand.

The Orange Riots In Belfast

Henry Joy McCracken

Folk-song crosses divides and transcends barriers. Socially it can be enjoyed by many, either as casual listeners or participants. Political songs, however, do not conform to these generalisations. They are intrinsically divisive, setting the green and orange factions against each other, often with tragic results. Political songs represent just a small fraction of the vast repertoire of folk-song. They were not often published on ballad sheets and scarcely ever in chapbooks. The main reason for this was that these publications crossed the political divide and could be purchased by anybody irrespective of creed. Most political songs were published in songbook collections such as *The Orange Songster, A Collection of Loyal Songs,* or *Paddy's Resource* and *The Harp of Erin.*

The cornerstone of the orange song tradition was the victory of King William over King James at the Battle of the Boyne in 1690. For the green tradition it was the 1798 Rebellion and the struggle of the United Irishmen to free Ireland from English rule. Even today these battles are potent symbols.

Despite the fact that the green and orange factions are so diametrically opposed politically, their songs contain many similarities. Both traditions transmit their songs in publications as well as orally and the songs are delivered in a style of singing that is peculiar to Ulster. Even the same melody can sometimes be used by both sides such as in *The Orange Maid of Sligo* and *Avondale,* a green song about Charles Stewart Parnell. Both use the same phraseology to describe the battles they have fought and won against all the odds. There are songs about great feats of heroism, victory in sectarian skirmishes and battles to defend religion against oppression.

The main differences are that orange songs contain many biblical references and have detailed descriptions of rituals associated with the Masonic and Orange Orders. Where orange songs refer to King William, green songs have various heroes at different times in history such as Daniel O'Connell and Charles Stewart Parnell. Each side often manages to present two quite different accounts of the same incident.

During the last century faction fights continued unabated. Each wave of sectarian strife or political upheaval brought in its wake a plethora of partisan ballads to whip up support for one cause or another and to castigate the other side. In Belfast today these battles are still being fought and songs seething with hatred are, unfortunately, still alive and thriving.

39. Henry Joy McCracken

Henry Joy McCracken, Wolfe Tone, Thomas Russell, Samuel Neilson and Robert Simms were leaders of the United Irishmen. In May 1795 they climbed to the summit of Cavehill and, standing on the ancient site of McArt's Fort, they swore an oath: "Never to desist in our efforts until we have subverted the authority of England over our country and asserted her independence". Their proclamation still reverberates through Belfast almost two hundred years later.

The song recalls the defeat of Henry Joy and his army of five hundred at Antrim on 7 June 1798. After the battle he fled to Slemish, County Antrim, and then to Cavehill where he took refuge in David Bodle's cottage. On the following day he hoped to gain passage on a ship bound for America (not France as in the song) but was stopped on the way by the yeomen guard. Although disguised as a carpenter, he was recognised by one of them, a man called Niblock, who had been a former customer of the McCrackens' business, and arrested. He was tried, convicted of treason and hanged on a scaffold erected outside the Market House, High Street, Belfast, all on the same day, 17 July 1798. Burton's clothes shop on the corner of High Street and Cornmarket stands on the site of the Market House; some of the shop assistants will not go into one of the store rooms alone because they believe it is haunted by a ghost.

The song was written by P.J. McCall who wrote *Boolavogue* and the melody was added by Cathal O'Byrne using George Petrie's air *The Belfast Mountains*. It is written from the point of view of Mary Bodle, who was Henry Joy McCracken's lover and had a child by him.

Henry Joy McCracken

It was on the Belfast Mountains I heard a maid complain
    And she vexed the sweet June evening with her heart-broken strain,
Saying, "Woe is me, life's anguish is more that I can dree,
    Since Henry Joy McCracken died on the gallows tree.

"At Donegore he proudly rode and he wore a suit of green,
    And brave though vain at Antrim his sword flashed lightning keen,
And when by spies surrounded his band to Slemish fled,
    He came unto the Cavehill for to rest a weary head.

"I watched for him each night long as in our cot he slept,
    At daybreak to the heather to MacArt's fort we crept,
When news came from Greencastle of a good ship anchored nigh,
    And down by yon wee fountain we met to say good-bye.

"He says, 'My love be cheerful for tears and fears are vain,'
    He says, 'My love be hopeful our land shall rise again.'
He kissed me ever fondly, he kissed me three times o'er,
    Saying, 'Death shall never part us my love for evermore.'

"That night I climbed the Cavehill and watched till morning blazed,
    And when its fires had kindled across the loch I gazed,
I saw an English tender at anchor off Garmoyle,
    But alas! no good ship bore him away to France's soil.

"And twice that night a tramping came from the old shore road,
 'Twas Ellis and his yeomen, false Niblock with them strode,
My father home returning the doleful story told,
 'Alas,' he says, 'young Harry Joy for fifty pounds is sold.'"

"And is it true," I asked her, "Yes it is true," she said,
 "For to this heart that loved him I pressed his gory head,
And every night pale bleeding his ghost comes to my side,
 My Harry, my dead Harry, comes for his promised bride."

Now on the Belfast mountains this fair maid's voice is still,
 For in a grave they laid her on high Carnmoney Hill,
And the sad waves beneath her chant a requiem for the dead,
 The rebel wind shrieks freedom above her weary head.

40. Annie Moore

The Belfast *News Letter* of Tuesday 14 July 1835 reported that

> On Saturday evening considerable crowds paraded in the neighbourhood of Sandy Row... on Sunday Orange arches were found to have been thrown across the street leading from the Saltwater Bridge to Barrack Street.... Towards evening the opposite party assembled and erected a green arch across the street near the head of Barrack Street.

Confrontation was followed by sectarian rioting. Police were called in but could not cope with the situation so they sent for the military to help them. They immediately tore down the green arch, but when they attempted to pull down the orange arches they met with "severe and protracted" resistance. Escalating violence was then directed at the military, who eventually read out the Riot Act. Rioting, looting and intimidation continued unabated; "stones were flying like a shower of hail". An order was given to open fire on the riotous mob: one man was shot in the head and recovered, another man had his arm fractured by a gunshot, six others were slightly wounded but one Ann Moore was shot dead.

A three-day-long inquiry was held into the riots. It was revealed that Ann Moore and her friend Mary Moffet were on their way from Pound Street to visit a friend in Sandy Row and were caught up in the rioting and subsequent shooting. Neither party was involved in the rioting. The verdict of the jury was that she had died from a gunshot fired by the military in the discharge of their duty in quelling a riotous mob. The *News Letter* commented:

> It is truly lamentable to witness the atrocious spirit by which citizens of the same country and natives of the same town are actuated in regard to each other, merely because their respective creeds are called by different names.

Annie Moore

As I roved out one evening in the month of sweet July
Through shady groves and valleys and streams as I passed by
The small birds they sat mourning on each green shady grove
They joined their notes all with that youth lamenting for his love.

He tore his hair distracted oft times his hands he wrung
The tears ran down his rosy cheeks like a watery stream
But still he cried my darling's gone the maid that I adore
By a sudden call to her long home – will I never see her more.

She was a proper tall young girl scarce seventeen years of age
And in no riotous company was ever she engaged
Her comrade girl asked her out a-walking for to go
She took her to that fateful spot which proved her overthrow.

It was on the twelfth day of July in the year of thirty-five
It ne'er shall be forgot by me as long as I'm alive
It was that day that very day my love was torn from me
She was the rose of Belfast town and the flower of this country.

It was on the twelfth day of July orange arches we did form
And Harvey and his cavalry thought to cut them down by storm
But all their efforts were in vain for we would not comply
And as we advanced "No surrender" was our cry.

When riding forth to cut them down we received a mortal blow
You know a stone from David's sling did lay Goliath low
Then the Light Infantry got an order to fire a round of ball
It was at that fatal moment my true love she did fall.

A ball it entered in her breast and pierced her body through
And gently fell and waved her hand she could not bid adieu
As I held her milk white hand in mine my breast being filled with woe
To see those lips I oftimes kissed now whiter than the snow.

Annie Moore was my love's name of credit and renown
She was the flower of this country and the rose of Belfast town
The Protestant cause she dearly loved – William's sons she did adore
And round her neck even to the last she an orange ribbon wore.

The Protestants of Belfast turned out like heroes brave
To carry her remains to the cold and silent grave
And many of those heroes that day in tears were found
At the leaving of her residence convenient to the town.

Her dear friends and relatives their lost one they now deplore
Likewise her comrade girl was a-walking round the shore
Their many hearts are merry while my poor heart is dry
For it makes me sigh when I think of the twelfth day of July.

41. The Battle Of The Navvies

42. The Orange Riots In Belfast

The year 1864 was a traumatic time in the history of Belfast. Sectarian riots which began on 8 August continued unabated and with ever increasing violence until the 23rd. Never before had there been rioting on such a scale with widespread shooting, intimidation and looting of gunsmiths, resulting in death, injury and destruction. The protagonists in these disturbances were the Protestants of Sandy Row and the Catholics of the nearby Pound area (now the Divis Flats area).

It all began when large crowds of Catholics went to Dublin to celebrate the laying of the foundation stone for a statue in honour of Daniel O'Connell. That evening in Belfast

The effigy of Daniel O'Connell was burned on the Boyne Bridge – the name given to the new railway bridge by the Sandy Row men. The burning mass was elevated on the bridge while the train conveying the excursionists from Dublin passed under it.

This incident was followed by the burning of a coffin which was supposed to contain the ashes of the effigy... a full mounted coffin was procured and after parading about with it for some time, they set fire to it and threw it into the Blackstaff.

Emotions were already highly charged and this incident signalled the start of the vicious faction fighting. Monday 15 August was a holy day and therefore a holiday for Catholics. At about 11.30 in the morning

Large crowds of persons principally navvies engaged in the excavations of the New Docks made St. Malachy's Chapel their rendevous... armed with tremendous bludgeons, pistols, guns and formidable knives.

There were upwards of four hundred in the crowd which headed for the centre of the town and onwards to North Street, not stopping until they reached Brown Square School, which was full of children.

At a given signal they rushed towards the Brown Square School...

the dastardly mob hurled stones and brick bats through every window... two or three shots were fired into the school.

Word quickly spread to the local men working in nearby foundries. They rushed out to give chase,

springing upon the navvies like tigers, striking terror into their souls... in Brown Street, Brown Square and Melbourne Street hardly a pane of glass was left.

The Protestant mob headed for St. Malachy's to seek revenge:

a desperate fight with fists and stones. Bullets were fired.

The two factions were eventually separated by a troop of cavalry.

By 16 August "the disturbances waxed worse and worse" and by midday on the 17th all shops in the town were shut, mills were partially or completely stopped and the streets were empty. Intimidation of Catholics in Protestant areas and vice versa occurred on an enormous scale. It was reported that "people have given up the idea of sleeping at night".

On Thursday 18 August the navvies returned to work at the docks but tensions were still running high. They finished work at two o'clock in the afternoon and armed themselves with spades, shovels, pickaxes and firearms. They were confronted by Protestants from the local foundries. These men were soon joined by ironworkers, shipwrights and carpenters from the shipyard. The navvies, finding themselves outnumbered, started to retreat, but once again found themselves hemmed in by the docks. Many tried to cross the River Lagan up to their waists in water, others took to the surrounding slob-lands through mud and water. They were hotly pursued, some as far as Whitehouse. Again the cavalry intervened to separate the factions. The ship carpenters were jubilant at thrashing the enemy and the battle of the navvies was the turning point in the fortnight of riots.

By 19 August the *News Letter* commented "at last there is some hope that the people of Belfast are to have peace". Rioting eased, tension diminished and normality crept stealthily back. However, cooperation was required between the fighting factions and on 23 August "a deputation waited upon the ship carpenters and navvies. By both sides promises were given that they would remain in peace."It was this pact that ended one of the most turbulent and traumatic eras in the history of nineteenth-century Belfast.

The following two songs re-enact this historic fortnight. The first song gives the Protestant point of view from the ship carpenters while the second song obviously emanates from the Daniel O'Connell faction.

The Battle Of The Navvies

We burnt the Bully Beggarman[1] – for him our scorn expressed,
And at the gate of Friar's Bush we laid him down to rest;
And from ten thousand people an indignant cry arose,
That we were crushed by Government, while petted were our foes!

And when we burnt the Beggarman, we thought it well to join
To raise a noble monument to William of the Boyne:
But angry grew Mick Kenna[2] and he wrote his anger down,
That he might raise the Navvies for to desolate the town.

And soon the Navvies left their work; and then the raging crew
Went marching up and down the streets with pike and pistol too:
There was danger in their faces, by sectarian hatred nursed,
And horror went before them like a cloud about to burst.

The shops were closed for safety in the middle of the day;
The streets were near deserted – people dreaded an affray
But onward went the Navvies like demons of misrule,
And they paused to show their valour beside an Infant School!

And there they fired their pistols, and heaps of stones they flung
Right through the shivering windows, to massacre the young;
And they only paused from ruin when they saw the gallant foe
Rush like a mountain torrent from the Foundry of Soho!

They fled like demons to their dens – in running they excel,
But forth again they issued when the evening shadows fell;
And many an honest citizen was reft of all he had,
By the brutal, plundering Navvies, by Mick Kenna driven mad!

Oh shame upon Mick Kenna! he's a stranger to our town;
He's disloyal to his Clergy, and disloyal to the Crown;
His tongue, like a malaria, sends a poison with his breath;
It was he who fired the Navvies to ruin and to death!

But woe to you ye Navvies! for before another sun,
You will sup a heap of sorrow for the ruin ye have done;
We'll come upon you like a storm, or like a sudden flood,
And send you, helter-skelter, writhing, wriggling through the mud.

They sent unto the Island, and they challenged us that day;
For they had guns and pistols to begin a bloody fray;
Our arms we had to find them, but we didn't dally long,
And we marched upon the Navvies in three columns stout and strong.

Brave Charley led us onward, bold Dick, and gallant Roe,
And like a bounding avalanche, we swept upon the foe;
The Navvies fought like bull-dogs, but we swore to put them down,
The assassins of the children, the despoilers of the town!

Some struggle in a deadly gripe, some load away and fire;
Ho! ho! the Navvies show their backs, and down the bank retire;
Some leap into the river, some are scrambling through the mud,
And our noble fellows follow to the margin of the flood!

They scatter o'er the slob-land – too warm behind to stay –
They struggle onward o'er the slime, and fling their guns away;
They call unto the holy saints to help them in their flight,
And all along the bank our boys were bursting at the sight!

'Tis not for us to claim the praise – we'll leave it to the town
To tell, by true acknowledgment, who put the Navvies down;
But many good folk do confess our work was done in time
To stay the murderous Navvies in their course of blood and crime!

And now that they have fled away, to keep our fair renown
We'll help the Special Constables and gentlemen of town
To crush those fearful Riots, which we are bound to say
Were called up by Mick Kenna and the Navvies in his pay!

The Orange Riots In Belfast

Rejoice sons of Erin all over the land,
Our noble procession was pleasant and grand,
And so rich indeed in Belfast me child
The friends of poor Billy it left them all wild.

> *Chorus*
> O'Connell he acted with such firm truth
> In return they only showed him gratitude,
> He earned all this and well it is known
> The sons of old Erin his loss may deplore.

The Emancipation first tortured them sore
But O'Connell's procession it grieved them far more.
On the 9th of August filled with bigotry
Near Belfast they burned brave Dan's effigy.

Chorus

Though he ne'er was a traitor indeed to the crown
But studied the peace in country and town,
Never the less those cowards you see,
They went to a helpless and poor Nunnery.

Chorus

Those cowardly assassins they are a disgrace
Now to honest Protestants in every place;
Not half satisfied as you may all perceive,
Till like rats sure they tore the dead out of the graves.

Chorus

O'Connell's procession the truth I declare,
Was a noble excuse for to murder and tear
Saint Malachy's Chapel all tattered and tore,
Their usage to females would grieve your heart sore.

Chorus

It's plain to the world they outstepped the law
To spill Roman blood without proper cause,
If processions should grieve them themselves should allow by
Their parading and walking on the 12th of July.

Chorus

In O'Connell's procession there was not a flaw,
But honoured and sanctioned by men of the law,
Not a party tune played to hurt them indeed,
The feelings of any colour, class or creed.

Chorus

The author of truth in high heaven so bright
Restore to us peace and bring all to right;
The stone it is laid and the price of it is blood,
The situation would grieve you through water and mud.

Chorus

Long live our good queen I hope she'll protect,
From daylight assassins her Roman subjects,
And look now with justice upon our sad case,
And check each disturber of the public peace.

Chorus

NOTES

Pepper Hill Steps

INTRODUCTION

1. J.J. Monaghan, unpublished thesis, Linenhall Library, p. 123:
   About the same time [1813] a white haired man roamed the streets singing and selling ballads . . . but as his ballads were generally of an offensive character . . . he was recommended to the attention of the police. Market day was the favourite time for ballad singers and many of those in the crowd that stood to listen had their pockets picked. By the year 1819 these itinerant singers had become a nuisance for on June 9th five ballad singers and one fiddler attracted crowds that facilitated the work of pickpockets. The police were asked to look into the matter.
2. A ballad singer was arrested in 1866 in Hillsborough, Co. Down, for selling *Erin's King or Daniel Is No More* and *Father Murphy And The Heroes of '98* – Belfast *News Letter* 19 April 1866.
3. One song called *Beresford Bob* had the following note on the melody: "To a dirty old tune that everybody knows and now vociferously chaunted in all quarters of the kingdom."
4. It would appear that Sam Elliot was witnessing a "Nigger Minstrel Show", a form of entertainment started in 1836 in England by "Jim Crow" Rice. It became very popular in concert halls and continued in popularity up to recent times in the form of "The Black and White Minstrel Show". In *Winkles and Champagne: Comedies and Tragedies of the Music Hall* (1938) M.W. Disher remarked (p.67) that "the songs that were originally orchestrated for the bones, the banjo and the tambourine are with us still and scores of others that we think of as typical of the British Music Hall were composed by the melodists of burnt cork."
5. Samuel M. Elliott, *The World As I Found It* (1887) p.22.
6. Mike Yates, "On the Halls", *Folk Roots* magazine, October 1986.

CAVEHILL

1. **The Belfast Mountains circa 1810** British Library Ref. L R 271 a 2. Also 11621 b 12 (12).
2. **The Belfast Mountains circa 1893** *English Folk Song Society Journal* AC 5167 Vol. 1 (1899-1904) pp. 170-171.
3. **The Belfast Mountains circa 1930** Sam Henry Collection No. 519.
5. **The Cavehill Diamond (2)**
   1. bea-ma-chres: grá mo chroí, my heart's beloved.

BELFAST TOWN

7. A New Song
1. Perry: a drink from the juice of fermented pears.
2. Charley: a night watchmen; also an insulting term for the better off.
3. Swipes: washy or turbid or otherwise inferior beer.
8. The Sights And Scenes Of Belfast British Library Ref. C 116 h 1 No. 157. A similar version of a song called *The Sights And Scenes Of Dublin* can be found in the McCall Collection in the National Library of Ireland.
1. Budget: a workman's bag or bundle.
2. Poll: a crop of hair.
3. Potale: completely fermented wash in distillation.
4. Counter jumper: a salesperson in a shop.
5. Waxy: slang for a cobbler.
6. Lapstone: shoemaker's stone held in lap to beat leather on.
7. Goose: a tailor's smoothing iron.

COTTON AND LINEN

10. Campbell's Mill Sam Henry collection No. 762.
1. Heckler: a man who drew fistfuls of flax fibres through a board which had sharp steel points to comb the flax into neat, regular strands, leaving it ready for spinning.
11. The Cotton Mill Song Collected from local singer and uileann piper Trevor Stewart.
12. Young McCance First collected in 1845 by John Hume of Kilmartin, Hillsborough, for his brother Canon Hume of Liverpool. The Hume collection of songs was eventually obtained by J.S. Corne who had also heard one version of the song sung by mill girls at Killead, Co. Antrim, and another at Castlereagh, Co. Down, in 1860. Over one hundred and twenty years later the song was still being sung as *At The Foot Of Davitt's Mountain* by John Quinn of Mullaghbawn, Co. Armagh. Sam Henry collected several versions known as *Divis Mountain* and *Drummond's Land*. Another song called *The Antrim Hunt* by William Percy (1826) contained the following verses:

> I now with best feeling smooth numbers advance
> The high estimation of Suffolk's McCance
> I hope he just knows that I'm still on the globe
> Would bow to his honour but shabby's my robe.

John Sinclair, Esquire, I now must advance
At least to an equal with comrade McCance
In the sports of the field few can either excel
And proud is the minstrel their praises to swell

See Sam Henry Collection No. 212 *Drummond's Land;* Hugh Shield's *Shamrock, Rose and Thistle;* No. 21 *David's Flowery Vale;* John Quinn of Mullaghbawn, Co. Armagh recorded *At The Foot Of Davitt's Mountain* or *You Know I Am A Stranger,* Outlet Archive Series O4S 3018. See also *Ulster Folklife* Vol 18 pp. 40 and 41, article by Hugh Shields; Ulster Museum booklet by Eileen Black, *John McCance of Suffolk (1772-1835).*
    1. Linen cloth was bought at a market in Tandragee.
    2. The Armagh coach was a normal coach service and an advertisement in the 1820 Almanac reads: "Lurgan and Armagh: Johnston's Belfast, Lurgan and Armagh Day Coach leaves Magee's 9 High Street Belfast on Tuesday, Thursday and Saturday at ten."
    3. Fusee: a type of pocket watch or a large-headed match for lighting a cigar or pipe in the wind.

13. You Might Easy Know A Doffer
    1. Pickers: used for poking out the broken ends of the thread that had become lapped around the rollers in the machinery.
    2. Rubber: a waist apron often made from hessian potato- or flour-bags to keep oil and water sprayed from the spinning frames off the workers' clothes.
    3. Scraper: used to scrape stubborn dirt away from the machinery which had to be scrubbed and cleaned down twice a month usually. The day allocated to this work was known as "Muck-up-Day".
    4. Scissors: the weaver and scissors were inseperable. "I could take my tea and all . . . open my purse and take my money out . . . and still the scissors were in my hand . . . " Betty Messenger, *Picking Up the Linen Threads.*
    5. Shawl: mill workers huddled in their shawls were a familiar sight on the streets of Belfast and were often referred to as "shawlies".
    6. Shuttle: a cigar-shaped implement with two painted ends used in weaving. Warp threads were stretched lengthwise in the weaving loom, and the cross threads or weft were shot across the warp using the shuttle to fabricate a woven web of material.

HORSE TRAMS

15. The New Tramway Ballad sheet in the British Library Ref. C 116 h 1.

The melody comes from an archive recording of Robert Cinnamond made by Sean O'Boyle in 1955 when Robert was seventy-one years of age. Robert Cinnamond was born in Ballinderry, Co. Antrim, in 1844. His only recollection of the song was a single verse and chorus.

16. **A Trace Boy On Ligoniel Hill** Written by Hugh Quinn (1884-1956) who was a school teacher in the Divis area of the Falls Road in Belfast. See *Rann* magazine No. 16 Summer 1952 for article by Quinn. The melody is a children's street song called *Green Gravel*.

    1. Crulge: a hump on the back.

18. **The Tramway Line** Ballad sheet from British Library Ref. C 116 h 1 No. 138/227.

CHILDREN'S SONGS

19. **Here's A Poor Widow From Sandy Row** From *Popular Rhymes And Sayings Of Ireland* (1931) by John J. Marshall MA.
20. **Jenny Jo** See also *Proc. Belfast Naturalists Field Club* Vol. iv Series II Part I 1893-1894 article by Clara M. Patterson.
21. **Round About The Punchbow**l From *Popular Rhymes And Sayings Of Ireland* as above. Other versions from *Proc. Belfast Naturalists Field Club* as above.
22. **Round About The Ladies** From *Popular Rhymes And Sayings Of Ireland* as above.
23. **Here's An Oul' Widow** From an article written by Sam Leighton and published in the *Belfast Telegraph* on 21 November 1921. Other versions from *Popular Rhymes And Sayings Of Ireland* as above.

THE MAIDS OF BELFAST

The following are the gods and goddesses frequently referred to in love songs:

Flora   goddess of flowers.
Cupid   god of love.
Diana   goddess of hunting; also sometimes used to refer to a horse-woman or a woman who is determined to remain single.
Venus   goddess of love.
Juno   wife of Jupiter and woman of stately beauty.
Aurora goddess of dawn.

28. **Belfast Town** Sam Henry Collection No. 45. The song was also collected by J.J. Marshall. See Queen's University Belfast Library Ref. LPR 8860/30. See also J.S. Crone Archive, Central Library Belfast for

another version entitled *Mary Of The Lagan Side*. A fragment of the song was recorded by Sean O'Boyle and Peter Kennedy in 1953 under the title *The Cavehill-side* or *Belfast Mountain* from Paddy McCluskey of Clough Mills, Co. Antrim, when he was seventy-three years of age.

THE RAKES OF BELFAST

30. **The Young Man Badly Walked** Ballad sheet from the British Library Ref. C 116 h 1 No. 187.
31. **The Sailor's Hornpipe In Caxon Street** Ballad sheet from Queen's University Belfast Ref. xff PR 8860/1.
33. **The Connaught Man's Trip To Belfast** Ballad sheet from the British Library Ref. C 116 h 1 No. 134.

THE PORT OF BELFAST

34. **Lovely Ann** or **The Loss Of The Ship Union** Published on a ballad sheet by J. & H. Baird, 20 Paul Street, Cork; also published in a chapbook by James Smyth, Belfast, 1826.
35. **The Loss Of The Lady Of The Lake** Ballad sheet published by Haly, Hanover Street, Cork.
    List of those saved from *The Lady of the Lake:* Crew – Capt. Grant, Mr Turner (mate), David Scott, John Tierney, James Ford, Wm McGlaughlan, Francis McMullan, James Stitt (boy), James Burris, Benjamin ____, Robert Least, James Grant (boys).
    Passengers – Nancy Davidson, Catherine McEntire, Margaret Duff, John Jones, Robert Cringle, John Cox, James Foster, James McCord, Robert Davison, Alexander Atchison, F. McGaragan, J. Douglas, John Beard, W. Armstrong, C. McReilly, R. Griffin, J. Griffin, Marshall Bailiff, Charles Rice, John Cunningham, H.S. Wright.
    Abstract of those saved – 12 in long boat with Capt. Grant; 8 in stern boat with mate; 13 in the boat *Harvest Home;* 1 saved by the *Lima.* Total saved 34; perished 197; total 234.
37. **The Brave Queen's Island Boys** Ballad sheet printed by Nicholson, Church Lane, Belfast, from the Biggar Collection, Central Library Belfast Ref. J1 and J2.
38. **The Shipwreck On The Lagan Canal** Ballad sheet printed by Nicholson, Church Lane, Belfast, from Queen's University Belfast Ref. xff PR 8860/1.

POLITICS IN BELFAST

39. Henry Joy McCracken Colm Ó Lochlainn's *Irish Street Ballads* No. 60.

40. Annie Moore From a ballad sheet printed by Nicholson, Church Lane, Belfast, in the Linenhall Library, Belfast.

41. The Battle Of The Navvies From a collection of ballad sheets in Cuttings Book No. 36 in the Linenhall Library, Belfast.

    1. Daniel O'Connell was frequently referred to as "the beggarman".

    2. Mick Kenna was the editor of the nationalist newspaper the *Ulster Observer* whose editorials were blamed for arousing nationalist feelings. His version of the 1864 riots gave quite a different view of what happened and who was to blame.

42. The Orange Riots In Belfast From a collection of ballad sheets in Cecil Sharp House, London. See also British Library Ref. 116 h 1 No. 92.

The songs in this book are now available on the cassette Belfast Town *(Ashgrove 002) Claddagh Records, 2 Cecilia St, Dublin 2.*